D1628227

Science
made
simple:

How? What? Why?

Answers to 500 questions, big and small

The Independent: Science made simple

Illustrations by James Robins

Published by Independent News & Media Limited, 191 Marsh Wall, London E14 9RS.
Printed in England by Cox & Wyman Ltd, Reading, Berkshire.

The science of Q&A

Every child goes through a phase of asking embarrassingly simple questions. Why is the sky blue? Why do we dream? Where did the Moon come from? Even the most educated adult can be stumped by such inquiries. But the curiosity behind them – and the urge to satisfy it – lies at the heart of science. Rainbows, too, were once a great mystery, until Isaac Newton split sunlight into the constituent colours of the spectrum.

Answering questions is what science is for; even though, in practice, it often throws up more questions than it answers. Those at the frontier of scientific knowledge well understand that the more they know about the Universe, the more there is to find out. Yet science has provided solutions to an extraordinary number of problems: some hugely important, some esoteric, and many less trivial than they at first appear.

This compendium of questions and answers is based on a weekly column first launched in *The Independent* more than a decade ago under the rubric "Technoquest" and, in later years, "What on Earth?". Prepared with the support of Science Line (a helpline, now sadly defunct, that promoted public understanding of science), it was inspired by the realisation that many readers had scientific conundrums niggling away at the back of their minds and would welcome a service that answered them.

The Q&A technique is now a popular format in newspapers and magazines and has even formed the basis of bestselling books. This collection seems an appropriate way to whet readers' appetite for the 12-part series of mini-books on big scientific themes – from evolution to particle physics – that will be given away with *The Independent* from Monday onwards.

Of course, not everything can be explained in a supposedly simple answer of a few sentences. Some questions are just too big. And often an answer is incomplete because of the difficulties of explaining something that requires a hinterland of knowledge. But the answers we publish here are as concise and as accurate as possible, and we hope that it will prove rewarding to read them.

John Keats once expressed his disappointment with Newton's reductionist explanation of the rainbow: he felt that the poetry of this ecstatic vision was lost once it was reduced to its prismatic elements. But does knowing the real reasons why a rainbow forms really make the spectacle any less magnificent? Many would argue the opposite: that it becomes even more awe-inspiring once you understand it.

By providing us with answers, science does us a great service in more ways than one. Of course, answers can be practical and useful, but they can also make us realise that the world around us is more even more mysterious and wonderful than our imaginations ever thought possible.

Steve Connor, Science Editor

The human condition

Why does hair go grey?

A hair is basically a tube filled with cells and pigment with spaces in between. When the hair is young, the spaces are filled with fluid and this keeps the pigment in place, so your hair keeps its colour. As we get older, our skin doesn't produce hair quite so well and the spaces become filled with air. The pigment is lost and the hair gradually becomes white.

Why do your hands go wrinkly in the bath?

Our bodies are covered with hairs, each of which has a gland (the sebaceous gland) at the bottom that pumps out sebum. This oily, waterproof layer stops water getting into our skin and keeps it supple. But the palms of our hands and our feet are hairless, so don't have this protective layer. This means that water can get into the skin of our hands and feet, and make them swell up. The skin swells into ridges because of the way the layers of skin are attached to each other.

Why do reaction times increase as we age?

Ageing seems to cause a general decline in sensory and perceptual skills. However, this might not be a direct result of age. Older people are more likely to have suffered disease or trauma and individual differences tend to increase generally with age. One feature clearly associated with age is a declining ability to see near objects. In addition, visual field and general acuity tend to reduce with age. There seem to be changes associated with age in the other senses, but the relationships are not clear. All of this will slow reaction times. In addition, dementia causes degeneration of nerve cells in the brain. Dementia is not a normal part of the ageing process but the fact that it is more common among people over 60 gives older people a reputation for altered mental abilities.

What makes urine yellow?

The kidneys serve two major functions: they keep the salt content of the blood constant, and they filter waste out of the bloodstream. So, the main components of urine are salt, water and waste products. The major waste product from cells in the body is ammonia, and the major waste product from blood is a broken form of the "haem" part of haemoglobin, called bilirubin. In the liver, each of these is converted into a less hazardous form: ammonia is converted to urea, and bilirubin is degraded to urobilogens. Salt, water, and urea are all colourless, but urobilogens are yellow. So, if you drink a lot, your urine will be clearer, and if you get dehydrated, your urine will be darker yellow.

I donate blood. The people getting the blood will get a dose of my DNA. Will they always have it? If not, for how long will they carry it?

They don't get as much DNA as you might think. This is because only body cells actually contain DNA, and most of what's in blood is actually fluid. Of the cells that make up the blood, there are red ones and white ones. Red blood cells don't have any DNA because they lose it during development. This helps them to do their job more efficiently; because the job of red blood cells is to carry oxygen, they lose their DNA so they can fit more

oxygen in. White blood cells do contain DNA, but there are not that many in the blood, unless a person is fighting off an infection. The National Blood Transfusion Service usually refuses donations from people who are fighting off infection.

So, having said that people who receive blood transfusions do not receive much DNA, what happens to the DNA that they do receive? Generally, the cells of the blood are replaced fairly quickly. All of the donated cells will have been replaced within several months following the transfusion, which means that all of the donated DNA will have been broken down and the ingredients recycled.

Why do your veins appear blue from the outside of your body?

There are three reasons why you can see your blue veins from outside your body. One is that the skin and surface tissues can be quite translucent. This depends to a certain extent on the colour of the skin; it is more difficult to see veins through darker skin. The second reason is that the veins you can see are actually very close to the surface. You cannot see arteries in the same way (arteries carry oxygenated blood from the lungs) because arteries are buried deep inside tissue. But veins run along the surface of your tissues, often just under your skin, so they are easily seen. The best places to see your veins are your inner wrists, the backs of your hands, your inner elbows, your neck and upper chest and your legs, especially your feet.

The reason that veins appear to

be blue is because they carry blood that does not contain much oxygen in it. Veins carry the blood back from the respiring body tissues to the heart and lungs. The tissues have exhausted much of the oxygen that was carried in the blood, so the blood appears blue. Blood that has high levels of oxygen in it is bright red, and is transported through the arteries.

The third reason has to do with the nature of the skin rather than the blood or vein itself. Fair skin normally reflects the light that hits it. However, the longer red wavelength of light can penetrate further into the skin than the shorter blue wavelength before being reflected out. So the red light travels into the blood in the vein and is absorbed there. But the blue light ends up being reflected back before it reaches the vein and this makes the vein appear blue.

Is it possible to live on nothing but sunlight, Chinese take-aways and water?

The answer to your question is most probably "yes". The human body needs water and nutrients from food and the sun to survive. A Chinese take-away gives us essential macro-nutrients such as carbohydrates (from rice or noodles), fats and proteins (from meat and oil) and micro-nutrients, such as vitamins A, D, E and K (found dissolved in fats) and vitamin C, and the B vitamins which are soluble in water and found in many vegetables. The food and water would also provide essential minerals such as sodium and potassium. You'd have to vary

your choice of take-away now and then as eating the same meat all the time would not provide all the essential amino acids (protein building blocks) that the body needs. Eating processed white rice all the time would lead to a deficiency in vitamin B1 (needed for metabolism) and the disease beriberi, which causes muscles to malfunction, so brown rice or noodles would be needed for a change. The Sun breaks down a source of vitamin D under the skin, which is helpful for using calcium to build bones and nails. Sources of calcium in Chinese food are not abundant, but if you had clams or oysters in your dish, you'd be fine. Of course, the body also needs air, or more specifically oxygen, but I'd assume you'd have that. So you could survive on sunlight, varied Chinese food and water – as indeed the Chinese do.

Why do people blush?

Uncontrollable, severe facial blushing is a physical condition caused by overactivity in the so-called sympathetic nervous system, a system made up of nerves over which we have no control. These uncontrollable nerves may become especially active due to social and emotional stimuli and may be very embarrassing; people may blush while meeting friends in the street or paying in a shop. Suddenly the face turns deep red, turning an ordinary social situation into an embarrassment, making social and even professional life almost impossible. We also blush as a result of our emotions. Strong emotion causes an increase in blood supply to the face, which is why we look red. The colour disappears after a minute or so, as the sympathetic nervous system, and hence the peripheral circulation, returns to normal.

Of the energy consumed by a human, what percentage is lost as heat?

At rest, one produces 4 kilojoules (kJ) of heat per kg of body weight per hour. This is about 7,100 kJ per day for an average man (weighing 75kg), and 6,300 kJ per day for an average woman. Converting these figures to calories gives us 1,700 calories per day for a man, and 1,500 per day for a woman.

The comparison with the proportion of energy consumed depends on what a person eats, but average calorie intakes are 2,500 for a man and 2,000 for a woman. On that basis, about 70 per cent of the energy consumed is lost in the form of heat.

Why do men go bald?

It's because of a sex hormone, testosterone, which occurs naturally in all our bodies. All men produce about the same amount of testosterone – about 10 times as much as women – but some are more vulnerable to its effects than others. Testosterone causes baldness in the hair follicles that are sensitive to one of the hormone's breakdown products, DHT.

Every follicle tends to produce hair in phases – a growing phase followed by a shorter resting phase, after which the hair is shed, then a new one grows. DHT makes the follicles "rest" sooner and eventually shut down to become dormant. Treatments do exist – but you have to use them every day or the regrown hair just falls out again.

How long does it take to digest food?

Unless you are ill, it takes hours or even days to digest food. The complete passage from mouth to anus is called the "intestinal transit time" and varies from about 24 hours to anything up to three weeks, depending mainly on the fibre content. This is measured nowadays using X-ray opaque shapes in the food, or dyes. The 24-hour figure is from rural Africans and the three weeks is US college students.

Early work on this topic was reported in one of the first editions of The Lancet. In the study, strings were tied to bits of food, swallowed, and then pulled back up to see how they were getting on. It is important to realise that the stomach acts as a hopper to try to ensure a steady stream of food passes through the gut.

Sloppy, bland foods like porridge will pass quickly into the gut while foods with stimulating ingredients, such as Bovril or meat, stay longer, as do fatty foods.

The job of the stomach, and the rest of the alimentary canal, is to mix everything up as much as possible: nothing passes through separately, and it will be absorbed over a period of time.

Our digestion process is very efficient – the Victorian concept of indigestible food is outdated.

Do bald people get dandruff?

Dandruff is caused by bacteria, yeast and fungi on the scalp, and these can live without hair. However, dandruff is more common in people with hair, as hair helps trap heat and water, providing ideal living conditions for such bugs.

What causes us to feel hungry?

There are two ways your body tells you it is time to eat. First, your stomach feels physically empty, as if there is a hole in it, and it rumbles. Actually, your stomach rumbles all the time, but you only hear it when there's no squishy food in your stomach to absorb the sound.

The other way is by a signal in the blood. There is a bit of sugar in your bloodstream. Every time you eat, your body uses the food to fill your blood with sugar. The rest of your body uses the sugar in your blood as a fuel. If you haven't eaten for a while, then the amount of sugar in your bloodstream is very low. Your brain notices that there is not enough sugar in your bloodstream, and starts producing "hungry" thoughts. How the brain makes "hungry" thoughts, or how the brain makes any sort of thought at all, is still a mystery.

Why does foil make your teeth hurt if, say, you eat chocolate and there's some foil left on?

This is a well known phenomenon when metallic objects come into contact with fillings. If the object is made out of a different type of metal than the filling, there will be galvanic action between the two.

Galvanic action occurs because different types of metal have a different likelihood of becoming ions. In order for atoms in the metal to become ions there must be electrons available, usually from a solution such as water. So, if you have two metals, with different likelihoods of becoming ions, and water (or saliva) inbetween, electrons will move from one to the other. The movement of electrons is the same as saying that an electric current is flowing. So you get a tiny electric shock that sets off the nerve endings in your teeth – which hurts!

In an embryo, how do the cells begin to specialise? How do they decide, for example, to become brain cells?

This answer applies to mammals only. Other animals can have very different developmental strategies.

In the initial stages, the fertilised egg divides to form a ball of cells. Cell position in the ball gives the cue for the first differentiation step. Cells on the outer surface of the ball become one kind of tissue (which will contribute to the placenta only) and cells on the inside become another cell type, which will give rise to the baby that is born. It is believed that the number of cell contacts is the key feature: outside equals a few cell contacts, inside equals many.

Once you have two cell types, there is further scope for interaction. Some of the "outside" cells are in contact with "inside" cells, and some are not. This leads to another two different types of cell arising. And so it goes on in a cascade of increasing complexity. During that cascade, genes come into the picture. While every cell has the same set of genes, its position (outside/inside) determines which genes are read and used to make the proteins that the genes encode. Depending on which genes the cell uses, even more varying sets of genes are activated, and so on, leading to an astonishing number of different tissues such as brain cells, bones and others. Just from one fertilised egg.

How can we tell if a sound is coming from in front or behind when we have only two ears?

The outside of the ear, the pinna, faces forward and catches sound waves. It also has a number of curves that help the ear determine from which direction the sound waves are coming. If the sound wave is coming from behind you, it will bounce off the pinna in a different way from sound waves coming from in front of or above you. The reflection of the sound wave off the pinna changes the pattern of the sound wave in a particular way, which depends on the direction it has come from. The brain is able to tell the difference between these patterns and so can tell which direction the sound is coming from.

The human ear is less sensitive to sounds from behind the head because of the immovable, forward-facing pinna. Other mammals, such as cats, have the ability to move their ears so that they point towards the source of the noise.

Does the body really burn fat from the immediate vicinity of an exercised area? In other words, if I do loads of sit-ups, am I not just toning the stomach muscles?

The body doesn't really burn fat from the immediate vicinity of an exercised area if you are doing resistance work, eg, sit-ups, weights or toning exercises. All you are doing is strengthening and toning the muscle you are exercising which is beneath the fat. To burn fat you need to do cardiovascular exercise: running, cycling, swimming, etc. The optimum heart rate for burning fat is at 60-65 per cent of your maximum heart rate, which is roughly 220 minus your age equals beats per minute. So if you were 20, your maximum heart rate would be 220-20 = 200bpm, and 60 per cent of 200 = 120bpm, and 65 per cent of 200 = 130bpm. So the optimum fat-burning exercise for a 20-year-old is any aerobic exercise providing their heart rate is between 120 and 130bpm. Where you burn fat from is thought to be determined genetically, but basically men normally store fat on their stomach and women on their hips. So exercise is most likely to burn fat from those areas.

How many veins are there in the human body? Do all people have the same amount of veins?

Blood is pumped round our body by the heart and passes through several types of "tubes" before it comes back to the heart. Blood from the heart is first pumped through the tough, elastic arteries. The aorta, which is the main artery from the heart, branches to form the systemic circulation which takes oxygen to all body tissues. These arteries taper down gradually in size, until they branch into the capillaries which are very tiny thin-walled tubes where gas exchanges with the tissues take place. Veins, gradually increasing in size, carry the deoxygenated blood back to your heart.

The total length of all the blood vessels in the body is approximately 97,000km, or 60,000 miles – twice the circumference of the Equator. However, the majority of these vessels are actually capillaries, and it's very difficult to give exact numbers here. There are veins coming from all major body areas, but not everyone will have the same amount; the smaller you are, the less blood you have and so the less blood vessels you will need. However, everybody has veins and arteries which go to all the parts of the body, so that's at least 34 main veins, and many more smaller veins connecting with the capillaries.

Why are unsaturated fats better than saturated fats in terms of a healthy diet?

Saturated fats are considered "bad" in terms of diet because they raise blood cholesterol and contribute to cardiovascular disease. Cholesterol is not a fat, but a steroid. Blood cholesterol is produced in the liver from a variety of foods – but especially from saturated fats. High cholesterol foods include eggs and dairy

products, but only a fairly small amount of blood cholesterol comes from these.

We do need some cholesterol. It helps to produce vitamin D and is essential to many processes. But a lot of people manufacture too much blood cholesterol. This can lead to a heart attack or stroke.

If an organ is transplanted into someone, does that organ still retain the DNA from the previous owner, even if the organ grows larger?

A transplanted organ always retains the DNA of its previous owner. When an organ grows, it either "enlarges" already existing cells or its cells divide. In the case of enlarging, the cellular structures are extended using molecular compounds present in the body. The nucleus, which contains the DNA, is not affected by any of these processes. When cells divide, they do this in a process called mitosis, in which the genetic information – DNA – is duplicated with the rest of the cell. "Parental" and "daughter" cells are identical. Here, too, no alteration of the DNA is observed. In both cases the cells of the organ keep their original genetic information.

Why do men have an Adam's apple while women don't?

The Adam's apple is a structure made of cartilage in the front of the neck. It is part of the voice box (larynx) and is usually larger in men than in women – so both men and women have an Adam's apple. They are larger in men because during puberty the male sex hormone testosterone causes it to grow larger. Because of this, men have longer vocal cords and a deeper voice.

Why do your joints click?

No one is really sure what causes joints to click. There are a number of possible theories. Since the click is normally heard when the joint is moved or stretched, it is possible that the pressure of the synovial fluid in the joint cavity is reduced. This may create a gas bubble that makes a popping sound. Another explanation is that the sound is created by the separation of the joints' surfaces, which release a vacuum seal in the joint.

Are women better multi-taskers than men?

Probably. Studies show that, on average, women are better at dealing with several different stimuli at the same time than men are. The critical words in that sentence are "on average", which means that the average female score differs from the average male score, not that every woman is better than every man.

Evolutionary psychologists have suggested that this may be because in early human societies, women bore the brunt of childcare, so they had to respond to the demands of their children while remaining alert to danger and foraging for plant food. Men were responsible for hunting animals for meat, and so had to be mentally focused. But it's easy to devise theories like this; much harder to prove that they are correct.

Whose DNA was used to map the human genome?

The "genome" in the publicly funded human genome project does not come from one person. It was taken from a panel of 20 volunteers from a variety of ethnic and social backgrounds. Researchers collected tissue samples from the donors and the names were protected so neither donors nor scientists knew whose DNA was being sequenced.

The genome is different in every individual (apart from identical twins), but not very different. Around 99.99 per cent of our DNA is the same among humans. The map is an amalgam of the individual genomes. Since we all share the vast majority of our DNA, almost all of this map applies to everyone. But there will be differences. Only a few of the differences are in useful parts of the genome, and it is these that give rise to hair colour, blood groups and inherited diseases. Now that the genome has been mapped, geneticists will be able to locate more easily the differences in our genomes that makes us individuals.

What causes twin babies to be born conjoined, or "Siamese"?

No one is really sure. It is probably the result of a mistake during development that would normally produce identical twins.

When a single fertilised egg divides very early on, while the embryo is no more than a ball of cells, it can lead to identical twins – though often one dies and the other embryo develops normally.

Sometimes, however, both embryos develop, resulting in twins.

Conjoined twins result from the fertilised egg splitting incompletely, leaving some cells bridging the two developing embryos. That explains how the twins are physically joined. But it doesn't explain the "why". Usually when the fertilised cell fails to split completely, one or both of the embryos will be miscarried. Very rarely, the twins are born alive and conjoined. But, while conjoined twins are very rare, the splitting of a fertilised egg is not. So rather than ask what makes the egg split (which scientists do not know), perhaps we should ask how the body knows when to miscarry, and why this mechanism does not work in the cases of conjoined twins. Scientists do not know the answer to this question either.

Is one ear normally lower than the other?

It's quite common for parts of our bodies to be unequal in size, shape and balance. Feet, for example, are often different sizes. Ears are no more likely to be uneven (or even) than the other parts of the face or body.

Why, if you shut one eye, do you still see in 3-D?

You don't, really, but your brain supplies the missing information, so you get the impression that you are still seeing an image with depth. Depth perception still isn't fully understood, but our brain can use pictorial clues such as the angle an object forms on our retina. Other clues include the brightness of the object; if it is brighter, it will usually be nearer, so light and shade can also be important. There are also physiological clues such as when you focus on something close, the shape of the actual lens changes. To check if you are really seeing in 3-D when you have one eye shut, try moving your head from side to side, or touching objects at varying distances.

When you exercise, does the blood supply to the brain increase or decrease?

Neither: it stays the same. The average heart pumps five litres of blood around the resting body every minute. Around 750 millilitres of this go to the brain and 600 millilitres to the muscles being used. When you exercise, the heart works harder – shifting a staggering 17 litres around the body. Of this, 14,000 millilitres go to the muscles, but 750 millilitres still go to the brain.

How is the skeleton held together?

The bones which make up the skeleton are held together by a support system consisting of skeletal muscles, ligaments, tendons, and cartilage. The skeletal muscles mean we can move whenever we feel like it. Ligaments join one bone to another, across a joint – without ligaments, joints would become dislocated very easily. Tendons join muscles to bones, across a joint. Some tendons are quite large and can be felt easily: the Achilles tendon at the back of the ankle and the two hamstring tendons at the back of the knee joint are good examples. Cartilage, or gristle, is a smooth, tough and flexible substance which is found in joints such as the knee. It covers the ends of bones at joints to allow smooth movement as the bones move against each other.

What are bones like inside?

Large bones, such as the thigh bone, have a hard, thick, outer layer and a soft middle called the marrow. The cylinder formed by large bones gives them great strength: they can support heavy weights without bending and breaking. Bone needs to be strong to stand up to the stresses of supporting and moving the body. Yet the bone itself is not solid. It forms a microscopic honeycomb which leaves lots of spaces for nerves and blood vessels.

Under a microscope, it is clear there are two basic sorts of bone. Compact bone is dense and heavy, but very strong. It is found in load-bearing areas such as the shafts of the long bones of the body (eg, the main part of the femur, or thigh bone).

The second type of bone is called spongy bone. This has a much more open structure and tends to be lighter than compact bone. Spongy bone is found in growing regions and in large masses of bone such as the head of the femur, which fits into the hip socket.

How much of my body is muscle?

In a normal adult, about two-fifths of the body weight is muscle. The actual figure depends on the individual. Most teenagers have slightly less muscle: more forms as the body matures.

Which is the smallest muscle in the body? Which is the largest?

The smallest muscles in the body, like the smallest bones in the body, are in the middle ear. Called the stapedius and the tensor tympani, these tiny muscles allow the delicate hearing apparatus to move so that we can hear sounds clearly.

Identifying the largest muscle is more difficult. The most powerful muscle is probably the gluteus maximus – the muscle that makes up the bottom; the longest is the sartorius, which runs from the hip to the knee; and the largest in surface area is the latissimus dorsi, the broad muscle that covers the back.

How many bones are there in the human body?

An adult skeleton contains 206 distinct bones: 26 in the vertebral columns, eight in the cranium, 14 in the face, seven other skull bones, 25 in the sternum and ribs, 64 in the upper limbs and 62 in the lower limbs. The stirrup bone, one of the three auditory ossicles in the middle ear, is the smallest: it is between 2.6mm and 3.4mm long, and weighs from 2.0 to 4.3mg.

What's the difference between white matter and grey matter?

Different areas of nerve tissue in the central nervous system are either grey(ish) or white. Grey matter contains nerve cell bodies:

their nuclei are responsible for the grey colour. Grey matter also contains other cells and some nerve fibres, and it forms the surface layer of the brain and an area deep inside the brain, as well as the central column of the spinal cord. White matter consists largely of nerve fibres which are covered by a white, fatty insulating material called myelin. It is the insulation that gives the tissue its white colour. White matter forms a layer between the two areas of grey matter in the brain, and encloses the column of grey matter in the spinal cord.

What causes colour-blindness, and why is it mainly a male problem?

Colour-blindness occurs when cones – the light sensors in the retina that respond to colour – are damaged. There are three types of colour-sensitive cones, responding to either red, green or blue light. Activation of combinations of these three lets us perceive all the colours of the rainbow. Loss of just one type of cone disrupts your colour vision; loss of two turns the multicoloured world into black and white. A colour-blind person can see clearly, but cannot distinguish certain colours, most frequently red or green (sometimes both). Red/green colour-blindness is mainly a male problem: about 8 per cent of male western Europeans are colour-blind. Of these, about 75 per cent are green colour-blind, and about 25 per cent red colour-blind. The gene(s) responsible are on the X sex chromosome, so men can inherit it from their mothers, but a woman

has to get the fault from both parents, which is much rarer.

Why does rubbing an injury make it hurt less?

If you get hurt, your first response is generally to rub the area vigorously until the pain ceases. The rubbing activates receptors in the skin which then act on endorphin-containing nerves. These release endorphins – the body's natural painkillers – and help to stop the pain. Eventually, if the rubbing doesn't work, you may have to resort to painkillers such as paracetamol and aspirin.

Why does the voice sound different when recorded?

Normally we hear our voices through the bones in our skull. The vibrations that we hear come through our own bones. When you record your voice and play it back, it sounds different because you hear the vibrations that have travelled through the air.

Are there sounds you can't hear?

Yes. A young child's ears can hear up to 25,000 hertz or more – the pitch (frequency) used by bats hunting for insects to eat. As we get older, we can only hear lower frequencies: by 13, most people can only hear sounds below 20,000 Hz. Adults, especially those who have abused their hearing by working in noisy places, lose even more of the top frequencies, and some older people can only hear sounds below 5,000 Hz. Luckily, most of the sounds in speech are in the range between 300 – 3,000 Hz, so nearly everyone can still communicate. Human ears are most sensitive to sounds around 3,000 Hz. Maybe it's no coincidence that this is the pitch of a smoke alarm – and a baby crying.

Low-frequency sounds below about 100 Hz feel more like a vibration than a note. The transformers in electricity substations vibrate at 100 Hz; you'll need to listen carefully, as your ears don't respond so well to such low frequencies, which sound more like a buzz than a note. A bee's buzz, for example, is about 20 Hz.

Why do we have five digits, not four?

The earliest four-footed animals – tetrapods – did not have five fingers or toes. Of the three we know well, Acanthostega had eight on each appendage, Ichthyostega seven and Tulerpeton six. Subsequently, about 370 million years ago, tetrapods split into two major lineages – one that eventually gave rise to modern amphibians (and a lot of extinct ones) and one that eventually gave rise to mammals, birds, dinosaurs and lizards. At this time, the number of toes on the foot stabilised at five, although some groups have subsequently lost some toes. In the hand, however, something different happened. In the line going to amphibians, the number of fingers stabilised at five. In the line going to reptiles and mammals, fingers also stabilised on five. Scientists are still trying to deduce why.

Digit formation in mammals and birds is controlled by overlapping sets of genes, called hox genes. Older forms of life, such as fish, do not have hox genes. A genetic mutation must have occurred which spurred the development of fingers and toes in the line that led to tetrapods.

How many cells are there in the human body?

About 50 million million (5×10^{13}). But although some cells, such as nerve cells, do not divide in the normal human adult, many others – such as blood cells – can and do divide in response to different challenges. Also, people vary in size and so must have different numbers of cells in their organs.

What is hair made of?

Hair is made from cells called epithelial cells, which are arranged in three layers. The innermost layer is the medulla, the middle layer is the cortex and the outer layer is the cuticle. The medulla is mainly soft keratin (a protein) and the cortex and cuticle are mainly hard keratin. This structure has great strength – a strand of hair is stronger than an equally thick strand of nylon or copper wire.

What determines how tall you grow?

Your adult height is determined by genetics and nutrition – with genetics playing the major part. If you are tall but your parents aren't, it's very likely that somewhere along your family line you had tall relatives, so the genes for a tall person are there even though your father and mother are of average height. But nutrition can also be a factor. Some researchers are testing whether there is a particular stage during development when a good diet can greatly affect your height.

Nutrition becomes a limiting factor on height only when malnutrition occurs or there is a lack of essential vitamins and minerals; so it's only partly true that there is a relationship between how much you eat and your height.

How much heat does the human body give off?

Curiously, men typically give off more heat than women – between 158 and 167 kilojoules per square metre of skin in men and 150-158 kilojoules per square metre in women. Adult men have about two square metres of skin, and so give out about 326 kilojoules from their bodies each hour – that is, just over 90 watts.

What makes us sleepy?

A tiny, pea-like blob at the base of the brain – the pineal gland – seems to be important. It produces a chemical, melatonin, particularly in late evening, and this makes us feel sleepy. Scientists are trying to find out more about such substances.

What is the recommended daily intake of salt for an adult?

Our bodies need 1 gram of sodium chloride (salt) a day to survive. The UK average intake for adults is 8 to 10 grams a day. For health reasons,

it is recommended that this be reduced to 5 to 6 grams – equivalent to a slightly heaped teaspoonful.

Do ears continue to grow after maturity?

Yes, earlobes can continue to grow, but generally once the head has stopped growing, so do the ears.

What is the funny bone?

The funny bone is actually a nerve which runs through a groove in a bone very close to the surface of your skin. It's called the ulnar nerve because it runs through the ulna, the outer of the two bones of the forearm. The ulnar nerve provides sensations for the wrist and hand.

At the elbow, the ulna sticks out, and both it and the ulnar nerve are very close to the skin, making them easy to bump or knock. If the nerve itself is hit, you get a very painful physical reaction, and when things hurt a lot, you get very emotional, which means you laugh (or cry, or both) a lot.

Why are women's voices higher than men's?

The larynx, or voice box, in the throat has a mucous membrane that forms two pairs of folds: an upper pair (the "false" vocal cords) and a lower pair (the "true" vocal cords). The false vocal cords hold the breath against pressure from beneath – say, when you strain to lift a heavy object. They do not produce sound.

The true vocal cords do produce sound. Under the folds are bands of elastic ligaments stretched between pieces of rigid cartilage like the strings on a guitar, with muscles attached to both the cartilage and the true vocal cords.

When the muscles contract, they pull the elastic ligaments tight, stretching the vocal cords out into the air passageway; this narrows the space between them. Air directed against the vocal cords makes them vibrate, creating sound waves in the air in the throat, nose and mouth. The greater the air pressure, the louder the sound.

Pitch is controlled by the tension of the true vocal cords. If they are pulled taut they vibrate more rapidly, creating a higher-pitched sound. Male sex hormones mean the vocal cords are usually thicker and longer in men than women; they therefore vibrate more slowly, giving men a generally lower range of pitch than women.

How does the retina work?

The retina, at the back of the eye, is a complex structure which has a deep layer of light-sensitive cells called rods and cones, a middle layer of bipolar neurones and a surface layer of ganglion (nerve) cells. The neurones connect the rods and cones with the ganglion cells, fibres which join to form the optic nerve.

This means that the front surface of the retina, which is about the size of a postage stamp, is not the light-sensitive part, because it is covered with blood vessels and nerve cells. But the brain ignores these obstructions; we do not see them as part of our image of the world. Instead, the back is the light-sensitive part, and the surface acts as a projection screen. The rods and cones capture the light, which is transmitted to the brain via the optic nerve.

We cannot see an object whose image falls on the retina at the point where the optic nerve leaves the eye. It contains no receptor cells, and so any light striking this small area is not picked up. This is why we call it the blind spott.

Is it true that the eye provides evidence of "intelligent design"?

If anything, it suggests the opposite. It seems unlikely that a Higher Being would have designed a retina that is, in effect, back to front, with incoming light having to penetrate a tangled mass of nerves before it reaches the light-sensitive cells at the base. But the eye does suggest how blind natural selection works on random mutations within existing structures.

How and why do we sneeze?

We sneeze to clear irritating material from our upper air passages. This can be dust, pollen or snuff, or excess mucus blocking the nose when we have a cold or hay fever. Sneezing is a reflex action that blasts air out at up to 103mph to clear the air passages. Pain receptors in the cells lining the upper respiratory tract are triggered by the dust or mucus and instruct the medulla (the base of your brain) to make you sneeze.

The sneeze itself is just a very powerful out-breath. The vocal cords are kept shut till the pressure in the chest has risen, and then the air is suddenly allowed to escape upwards, being directed into the back of the nose by the soft palate. But the 103mph of a sneeze is nothing compared to the 600mph that a cough gets up to.

What is Alzheimer's disease?

The disease was first described in 1907 by a German neurologist, Alois Alzheimer, and is a form of dementia (madness) that mainly attacks older people – some 4-5 per cent of those over 65 have symptoms of it but it sometimes strikes those in their forties or fifties. It is the fourth largest cause of death, after heart disease, cancer and stroke, and there are 700,000 people with dementia in the UK; this number is likely to double by the year 2021 because the average age of the population is increasing.

Citrus fruit does not grow in the Arctic, so how do the Inuit Eskimos avoid scurvy?

Earlier this century, Vilhjalmur Stefansson argued that it was possible for people of European stock to live for long periods on a traditional and entirely carnivorous Inuit diet, and that many Arctic explorers had developed scurvy (caused by lack of vitamin C) because they would not follow the Inuit and trust their instinct and experience.

He and a colleague volunteered to subsist on nothing but meat, under medical supervision in New York, for one year starting in February 1928. They each consumed between 100gm and 140gm of protein a day, with the remaining calories coming from fat. Both men remained in good health and showed no sign of scurvy.

It has been estimated that a traditional, daily Inuit diet, even without any plant material, would contain 40mg of vitamin C, enough to avoid scurvy. But some flora – including rose hips, a good source of the vitamin - grow in areas where the Inuit live.

Why is it dangerous to wake a sleepwalker?

When we sleep, we go through different phases. Sleepwalking occurs in the "slow wave" part of sleep, during which our bodies use little oxygen and have basically shut down. During this form of sleep the body cannot cope as well as usual with shock, so any sudden changes – such as being abruptly wakened – can be dangerous for people with heart problems.

Why does your nose go red when you are cold?

Cold causes your veins to shrink in order to cut down on the amount of blood near the skin (and so heat loss), which makes you look pale. But your nose helps to warm and humidify the air that you breathe, and needs a good blood supply to work properly. So, the veins in your nose are adapted not to shrink in the cold, making your nose much redder than the rest of your face in low temperatures.

How does a nerve signal pass between cells?

When the nerve signal (in the form of an electrochemical "potential" between the inside and outside of the nerve) reaches the end of an axon, it is passed on to the next nerve cell, or on to an effector cell, such as a muscle. The axon of one neurone doesn't usually make direct contact with the cell body of the next: the two cells are separated by a gap called a synapse. Information is transmitted across the synapse using chemicals called neurotransmitters, which cause electrical changes in the membrane of the next cell. The signal then passes along to the next nerve cell in the network.

What is in a nerve besides nerve cells?

Packed between the neurones are the glial cells. These make up the neuroglia, tissue which supports the neurone network, protecting it and providing the neurones with nutrients. Glial supporting cells make up about half the weight of the human brain, outnumbering neurones by 50 to 1. In other parts of the nervous system the proportion is much lower – about 10 to 1.

What's the technical name for a freckle?

A freckle is called a lentigo. Freckles are caused by certain cells producing too much melanin – the chemical that gives our bodies colour.

Why does salt make you thirsty?

When salt crystals, which have a very orderly structure, get the chance to dissolve in water, they take it – because the level of disorder (or "entropy") increases when the crystals become disordered ions in water. The drop in entropy when salt dissolves is much greater than for many other things – so salt preferentially takes water from other chemicals or states. Thus salt in your mouth or stomach sucks water from your bloodstream. This triggers sensors in the brain, which alert you that there's less water in your blood circulation. In other words, you feel thirsty.

What is the evolutionary advantage to Homo sapiens in having a prominent nose, as most other primates have flat noses?

The nose serves two main purposes: to moisten the air we breathe, and to warm it. Races from Equatorial regions tend to have flatter noses, as they don't need to put extra moisture into the air they breathe, whereas people who live in desert countries tend to have longer noses as the air is very dry, and needs more moisture added. On the other hand, races from colder countries, such as the Inuit and Tibetans, have flatter noses because the importance of warming the air you breathe is outweighed by that of not losing heat through your extremities.

It is difficult to establish an exact evolutionary advantage, as selective pressures vary between different people living in different environments, but the overall advantage compared with primates is that Homo sapiens roamed to practically every environment in the world – and adapted through selective pressures to survive in each particular environment.

How long does it take for the alcohol in a drink to reach your bloodstream?

On average it takes 20 minutes for alcohol to reach the bloodstream after the first drink, and then approximately 1 hour per unit after this. This varies per person depending on their tolerance to alcohol, of course.

How many hairs are there in a human cochlea?

The cochlea, a part of the ear that helps us hear, has about 15,500 separate tiny hairs that wave from side to side sending signals to our brain.

What is myelin and why is it important to nerve cells?

In vertebrates, specialised cells called Schwann cells wrap themselves round the long thin bits of nerve cells in the peripheral nervous system. The Schwann cells form a thick insulating layer rich in lipids (a sort of fat) called the myelin sheath. This insulates the axon, rather like the plastic layer round a copper wire in an electrical flex. Nerve cells with myelin sheaths are called myelinated nerves.

Curiously, there is a type of mouse which has a genetic mutation that means that it has no myelinated nerves. Without the insulation that myelin provides, nerve impulses passing along one nerve cell also affect nearby nerve cells, some of which connect to muscles. The affected mouse shivers and makes jerking movements as its muscles are stimulated.

People whose myelin sheaths are damaged as a result of multiple sclerosis can experience similar difficulties in controlling their muscles

What causes hiccups?

Underneath your lungs is a large muscle called the diaphragm. When it contracts, it pulls down on the lungs, making you breathe in. Hiccups result from a nervous reflex which causes your diaphragm to contract suddenly, making you breathe in involuntarily – generating a peculiar sound.

Why do doctors on TV tap the knee of a patient to see if their leg jerks?

They do this to test whether the knee jerk reflex – which helps the body to control the movement of the legs during running – is working properly. If it is, this gives the "doctor" information about how well the person's nervous system is working, and they test to see if it is working on both sides of the body. A reflex is a rapid, automatic response to a stimulus: pulling your hand away from a hot pan-handle is a reflex action.

A simple reflex involves communication between neurones in the peripheral nervous system and the spinal cord. The brain may be informed, but does not take part in the response.

Reflexes can also help to co-ordinate complex muscular events, such as swallowing.

The knee-jerk is a "stretch" reflex – one of many which work together to help us maintain an upright posture. You can test it by holding your knee suspended, leg down, and tapping the leg just below the kneecap. Your lower leg should lift automatically.

Is it true that cold weather stimulates urination?

Cold weather of itself would not directly stimulate urine production or excretion. But it does lead to reduced sweat production, so proportionally more water has to be excreted via the kidneys – hence, more visits to the toilet.

How fast does a signal travel down a nerve?

The speed at which a nerve impulse, or action potential, travels is known as its conduction velocity. In human nerve fibres, values range from 1 and 3 metres per second (2 to 6mph) in unmyelinated fibres (without a fatty sheath), and between 3 and 120m/s (6 to 270 mph) in myelinated fibres.

How do muscles work?

The mechanism that allows muscles to move is very complicated. Basically, each muscle is made up lots of fibres, each of which contains lots of individual cells, all long and thin. Each cell is a similar collection of tiny, long fibres lying next to each other.

These fibres are of two types. One has bits sticking out of it, along its whole length, which look a bit like the oars of a long-boat. The other is basically smooth, but with regular pits. When the muscle is still, the "oars" rest inside the "pits". When a nerve signal passes from the brain to, say, the arm, to reach up and scratch your nose, chemicals are released at the nerve ending and set off a complicated chain reaction inside the muscle. The end result is that the "oars" in one set of fibres move up and push into the next set of "pits", causing the muscle to contract.

Does eating fish make you brainy?

Possibly. There is some evidence that nutrients which are found at high levels in oily fish are important in brain development. The brain is rich in decosahexaenoic acid (DHA), a fatty acid which the body can produce, but not very efficiently. The best source for DHA is diet. It is found in meat and eggs and in particularly high levels in fish. Oily fish (mackerel, sardines, herring, tuna) are very high in DHA, whereas white fish (cod, plaice, monkfish) have high levels of DHA only in their livers.

It has been reported that DHA

improves eyesight, circulation and skin and that it can alleviate rheumatoid arthritis. There has also been evidence to suggest that it increases learning ability and visual awareness. Rats fed on DHA-rich diets learn to escape from mazes more quickly than those deprived of it; experiments on primates revealed similar results.

There is also evidence that premature babies fed on their mothers' milk have a higher IQ, visual acuity and dexterity than those fed on formula milk substitute.

This doesn't contain DHA, whereas human milk does. It seems that the intelligence-enhancing activities of a DHA-rich diet occur only between the fourth month of pregnancy and the ninth month after birth, during the development of the brain. It seems to be your mother's diet that has the strongest effect on your intelligence, not what you eat yourself.

Porters in Nepal carry heavy weights suspended from their heads, whereas Westerners tend to carry such weights suspended from shoulders, in rucksacks. Which is the better method?

Most rucksacks, or at least the larger ones, have waist straps to take most of the weight. In a well-fitting rucksack, most weight will be taken on the hips, with the shoulder straps just used for balance.

It is thought that this is better for you than using straps around the head, which put an enormous strain on your neck and back vertebrae – not the strongest parts of your skeleton. Your hips, on the other hand, as long as the load is spread evenly, can take quite a lot of weight before being damaged.

How do we hear sound waves?

The outer ear collects sounds which have been carried as pressure waves in the air. These waves make the eardrum (or tympanum) vibrate. Three small bones connected to the eardrum, called the ossicles, amplify the vibrations and pass them on to the cochlea.

The cochlea looks like a snail and is filled with liquid and lined by super-sensitive hairs. When vibrations hit the cochlea, the liquid inside starts to move, causing some of the hairs to sway. The movement of the hairs activates nerves attached to their bases, sending electrical signals to the brain where they are decoded into voice patterns, music and so on.

Is there such a thing as a bionic eye?

People may be either blind from birth or have lost their sight through disease or an accident. For those born blind, an artificial eye may not be all that useful as their visual cortex has not been trained to see. For those who have lost their vision later on in life, a bionic eye (an implant that replaces damaged retinal cells) may restore some of their sight.

Retinal implants are constructed from 25 electrodes just a thousandth of a millimetre thick, and incorporate a miniature solar panel. When the panels absorb light, tiny currents are generated in the implants which then stimulate the ganglion cells beneath, bypassing damaged retinal cells. So far, the implants have worked in animals and in one human volunteer who had gone blind through glaucoma.

The patient could see a light shone in the eye, and make out simple letters. If more electrodes are used, the wearer's vision might be even better. Next, the researchers will need to make an implant that does not corrode in the salty solutions of the eye, and will not slice into the retina (the implants are razor sharp as they are so thin). Researchers remain hopeful that eventually such implants may restore sight to some blind people.

Why do your eyebrows grow as you get older?

The continued growth of hair in men is thought to be due to the male sex hormones (androgens). Hair in different parts of the body varies in its sensitivity to androgens and eyebrows, noses, ears and patches on the top of the shoulders respond to continual high levels of the hormones. It therefore does not usually appear in women, who have much lower levels of androgens.

Why evolution should have produced them is unclear. There is, however, a hint from some species that females seek out males who are older because that shows they are good at surviving and so must have a fit set of genes. The males of these species develop outward signs of their age. Perhaps going grey and sprouting ear and nose hairs was once attractive to

women, and so men showing them were successful at getting their genes into the next generation.

How does the brain work?

The brain is far more complex than even the biggest supercomputers and there is still a lot we don't know about it. An average brain weighs 3lb (1.4kg) and contains about 100 billion nerve cells – about the same number as there are stars in the Milky Way. Each nerve cell has between 1,000 and 10,000 connections with other nerve cells, which are mediated by special chemicals. The number and pattern of connections in use at any one time depends on what we are doing. After the age of 20, our brains lose about 0.03 ounces (1 gram) in weight per year as nerve cells die and are not replaced. Luckily, some nerve cells duplicate tasks – so we don't lose function at once.

Are some people more likely to get addicted to drugs than others?

Many people use potentially addictive substances regularly without getting addicted (for example, the social drinking of alcohol), but others find themselves becoming dependent on their use. There may be additional reasons for the over-use of drugs, such as depression, and social or family environment may influence whether or not use turns into abuse.

Our genes may also have something to do with it, but research in this area is still at a very early stage. Almost certainly there is no single "addiction" gene.

What is synaesthesia?

It is an unusual condition in which the senses get cross-wired. A person with synaesthesia may see colours when they hear a sound, or actually taste words; stimulation of one sense, it seems, causes an inappropriate stimulation of another.

The most common form of synaesthesia is seeing or hearing words in colour. The condition affects about 1 in 25,000 people and is more common in women than in men, and more synaesthetics are left-handed than the population average, but the significance of this is unclear.

No one really knows what goes on in the synaesthetic brain. One theory is that the region of the brain normally receiving input from the ears also gets some information from the eyes.

Brain imaging shows that areas of the cortex which normally receive information from the eyes are also activated when the person hears a sound. This would suggest that there is some cross-wiring in the brain.

But other researchers argue that this is too simplistic, and that synaesthetics have an unusual limbic system (the centre of emotion in the brain). They suggest that the limbic system pulls together fragments of memories from all over the brain and pastes them together to produce a complete memory.

Normally we are not conscious of this process, but perhaps synaesthetics are. This may explain why inappropriate sensory data pops up in their mind.

Synaesthetics do not think of their unusual ability as a handicap. Most are sorry that the rest of us live in such a colourless world.

Can we lose our sense of taste and smell?

Yes, and people who go to their GP reporting a loss of either sense are, after testing, found to be either completely without smell or taste sensations or they may have a reduced sensitivity to particular tastes or smells. In some disorders of the chemical senses, the system may misread and distort a smell, a taste, or a flavour. Or a person may detect a bad smell or taste from a substance that is normally nice. Smell disorders are more common than taste disorders and both are potentially serious. A person with faulty chemosenses is deprived of an early warning that most of us take for granted. Smell and taste alert us to fires, poisonous fumes, leaking gas, and spoiled food and beverages. Smell and taste losses can also lead to depression because eating just isn't fun any more.

Some people are born with poor senses of taste or smell, but most develop them after an injury or illness. Upper respiratory infections and head injuries are frequently blamed. Loss of the sense of smell can result from polyps in the nasal cavities, sinus infections, hormonal disturbances, or dental problems. Loss of smell and taste also can be caused by exposure to chemicals such as insecticides and by some medicines. For example, many patients find that their sense of taste and smell is affected after receiving radiation therapy for cancers of the head and neck.

The extent of a particular person's problem can be determined by measuring the lowest concentration of a chemical that he or she can detect. A patient also may be asked to compare the smells or tastes of different chemicals or to note how the intensities of smells or tastes grow when a chemical's concentration is increased. Scientists have developed a "scratch and sniff" test to evaluate smell. A person scratches pieces of paper treated to release different smells, sniffs them, and tries to identify each one from a list.

In taste testing, the patient responds to different chemical concentrations: this may involve a simple "sip, spit, and rinse" test, or chemicals may be applied to areas of the tongue.

How much does the cortex of the human brain weigh?

The cortex has been estimated to contain about 15 billion to 25 billion nerve cells. That is about a quarter of all the cells in the brain. But these estimates are notoriously unreliable. We do know it is about 3 millimetres thick. So if about half the brain weight is nerve cells and the rest is fibres, and if one-quarter of the cells are in the cortex, it ought to be about one-eighth of the weight of the brain. That would make it about 150-200 grams – let's say about 6 ounces.

How many blood cells are there in an average person?

There are about 5 billion red blood cells in every millilitre of

blood, which gives a total of 245,000,000,000 (245 billion) in the average-sized person.

They are all sent around the body once every minute.

How fast do sprinters run?

Over short distances, the fastest sprinters can reach speeds of over 43km/h (almost 27mph).

Why do people dream?

Most dreams are based in familiar surroundings and are about events, emotions and thoughts recently experienced. Why we dream, though, is not clear. We know that the brain needs constant stimulation to work normally. One idea is that dreaming is a way of helping to maintain brain function during sleep, when the amount of brain stimulation from other sources is non-existent. Some people think dreams have meaning, but most believe they are just random thoughts in the brain.

Men have nipples, but are they used for anything?

Men's nipples certainly don't serve any important physiological function, unlike the nipples of women; rather, they are a hangover from the early days in the womb.

The fundamental differences between boys and girls do not begin to become evident until between the tenth and fifteenth week after conception. Prior to this, males and females in the womb are anatomically identical.

If the foetus carries a Y chromosome from its father,

hormones are produced which alter the internal "piping and ducts" to produce a boy. If the second chromosome is an X, then the foetus develops into a girl as a result of a different set of hormones.

However, by this point the nipples have already been formed, and they cannot be unmade. So they remain – as a legacy of the days when all life was "female".

Is a cold caused by a bacteria or a virus?

In a way, it is caused by both. Initially, the common cold is caused by a virus. That itchy feeling you get in your nose and throat when you first feel as though you have a cold is caused by the virus.

However, because it damages the inside of your nose and throat, bacteria can then cause further damage – when this happens, bacteria start to grow and cause further problems.

This is what causes the uncomfortable "bunged up" feeling a couple of days after you first get the sore throat. Only when your body manages to fight off the virus and the bacteria, do the signs of the cold disappear.

Is there any difference between fingernails and toenails?

Not really: they are very similar. Nails are also like hair in a lot of ways. They, too, consist of modified epithelial cells and are mainly composed of keratin.

Nails help protect the ends of the fingers and toes. The fingernails are especially important in humans

and primates because we use our hands so much. Nails allow us to grip and pick at things which soft skin would not permit: they also allow us to have a good scratch! The only difference that we know of is that fingernails grow faster than toenails, increasing in length by 0.5mm per week.

Why does blood turn a rust-like colour when it dries?

Blood contains small amounts of iron. When exposed to the air, this iron oxidises – in other words, its chemical make-up changes as the iron joins with the oxygen in the air.

This is exactly what happens with the iron that we use for constructing things does if it is not protected from the air.

In effect, therefore, it is true to say that our blood, just like iron railings or a car, rusts when it is exposed to air.

What happens to brain cells after they die?

A dead cell in the brain, or anywhere else in the body, starts to break down when it dies. Cell fragments are "eaten up" by the large white cells in the body, called macrophages. These surround the dead cell fragments and take them into their cytoplasm.

Lysosomes, enzyme-containing bags, are then emptied into the internal sac that contains the nerve cell fragment and it is digested. The macrophages use anything useful and get rid of the waste into the bloodstream. This waste ultimately goes to the kidneys for excretion.

What is the smallest bone in the ear?

The stirrup bone, one of the three auditory ossicles in the middle ear, measures between 2.6mm and 3.4mm in length and weighs from 2.0 to 4.3 milligrams – roughly the same dimensions as a grain of rice.

How do our eyes adapt to light and dark?

If you are in the dark, or in very dim light, for over half an hour, the rate at which photopigments in the eye are formed is much faster than the rate at which they are broken down. Your eyes are dark-adapted.

If your eyes are exposed to bright light for a long period of time, much of the light-sensitive pigment in the rods and cones is broken down and the sensitivity of your eyes to light is much reduced. In this situation, your eyes are said to be light-adapted.

The living planet

Is the world getting lighter or heavier?

The Earth catches around 500 tonnes of dust and stones every day as it travels through space. In its 4 billion-year history, it has put on about 16 million million million tonnes. This accounts for less than 1 percent of the Earth's total mass. But it has gained weight over the years.

Does it rain harder at the edge of clouds or in the middle?

During a rainstorm it tends to cloud over first before the rain comes, implying that rain comes from the centre of the cloud. But this really depends on what you mean by the edge of a cloud. Rain clouds seem to fill the whole sky and whether you can refer to these clouds as one or more is debatable.

Rain falls when the droplets acquire enough water to be too heavy to be held suspended in the air. At the edge of the cloud there is less water (ie, less cloud), and so

raindrops are less likely to form.

Small rain clouds tend to be pyramidal in shape and consist of a single convective cell. The intensity of the rain depends on the concentration of drops that are big enough for their terminal velocity to overcome the updraught which is associated with convection.

The size of the drops depends to some extent on the length of time that they spend growing within the cloud, and as this in turn depends on the depth of the cloud, bigger drops are produced towards the centre, where the cloud is thickest.

The same is true of rain associated with frontal systems. Common experience of the persistent rain associated with warm fronts suggests that the rain starts as drizzle from fairly thin cloud, and increases in intensity as the thickening cloud sheet passes overhead.

But large storm clouds, in particular those associated with tropical rain events, may have a more complicated structure, with many cells. Often the cloud regenerates at one edge as incoming warm, moist air is forced upwards over the cold, dense downdraught, which forms the gust front. In this case the active, leading edge of the storm will correspond to the most intense rain and the intensity will decrease as the remainder of the cloud passes overhead. In such a storm, maybe 30 per cent of the rain will fall in the first 30 minutes as the leading edge passes over. The remainder will fall with decreasing intensity over the next few hours.

What is the current number of species in the world?

About 1.5 million to 1.8 million species have been formally identified and named, but the actual number of species present in the world is far higher: the guesstimates at the moment are between 10 and 30 million, but some go as high as 100 million. Of these, more than 90 per cent are invertebrates. The World Conservation Monitoring Centre's records indicate that there are: 4,237 mammals; 22,000-plus fish; 9,672 birds; 4,000-plus reptiles; 6,500-plus amphibians; 460,000-plus plants; and more than 1 million invertebrates (though there are likely to be millions more).

Why don't lightning and thunder occur at exactly the same time?

Actually, they do: thunder and lightning always occur together in a storm. But most people aren't present at the point where the lightning hits. Instead, you usually witness the event some distance away. The light from the lightning travels much faster than the sound from the thunder, so the light reaches you almost instantaneously. But it takes about five seconds for sound to travel one mile. By counting the number of seconds between the lightning flash and the thunder, you can calculate how far away the storm is.

Why do runner beans always grow in the same direction? Mine always grow round the pole like a right-hand threaded screw.

Left- and right-handedness are often observed in nature. Some wild populations of beans curl to the right, others to the left. It's likely that the right-handed twining types were preferentially or accidentally selected by farmers over the past 5,000-10,000 years of domestication, so that now most runner beans in cultivation are right-handed.

What causes the Northern Lights?

The Northern Lights, or aurora borealis, are caused by the interaction of the solar wind of charged particles streaming out from the Sun, and the magnetic field which surrounds the Earth. Particles are trapped within the magnetic field until they enter the upper atmosphere, where they collide with molecules in the air. This generates the light. There is a greater chance of an aurora occurring when the Sun is experiencing its greatest activity.

The Sun goes through an 11-year cycle, and the chances of seeing an aurora are highest when sunspots are at their peak.

How fast is the Earth spinning?

It depends where you are. On the equator, where the circumference of the Earth is about 40,075 kilometres, the rotational speed with respect to an imaginary line through the Poles is about 1,670 km/h, or just over 1,000 mph. In the UK, where the distance travelled in 24 hours is only 26,000 km, we are travelling at 1,080 km/h, or 675 mph.

How many chemicals are there?

Chemicals and compounds are made up of different combinations of elements. We can say how many different elements there are, but you could argue that the number of compounds of these is infinite. To date, 116 elements have been discovered. Elements are the building blocks of other compounds. The number of compounds is growing all the time as scientists create new substances, so we can't name a figure.

Why do apples go brown?

When you cut an apple you're actually bursting open the cells that make up the apple. This releases an enzyme called phenoloxidase. This enzyme takes oxygen from the air and adds it to a chemical in the apples called tannin.

When oxygen and tannin are bound together, the tannin turns brown. Cooking or chilling the apple will stop it from turning brown. Vitamin C also stops the tannin from turning brown as it grabs the oxygen from the air before it can react with the tannin.

If everyone suddenly became vegetarian, would there be enough grain to feed them all?

Cattle are normally fed with grain, vegetables and grass. One hectare of farmland used for raising beef produces 20kg of beef protein. This same hectare used to grow wheat would yield 300kg of wheat protein. A football pitch-sized field can, in the same amount of time, provide meat to feed two people, maize to feed 10, wheat to feed 24 or soya beans to feed 61. Presently, 40 per cent of the world's grain is fed to livestock to produce meat – so if everyone turned vegetarian, food would not be a problem.

How was the Giants' Causeway (on the coast of County Antrim, Northern Ireland) formed?

The 40,000 hexagonal basalt columns are about 55 million years old, and were formed by cooling lava. As basalt lava flows cool, they slowly solidify from the liquid. The top and the bottom of the lava flow are cooled respectively by the air and by the rock over which it has flowed, while the interior is insulated and remains hot. So the upper and lower surfaces harden first. As the lava on the surface cools, it hardens, at randomly scattered centres. Basalt shrinks as it solidifies, so the solid area spreads slowly out as ever-increasing circles. At an equal distance between any two, the solidifying basalt will be pulled in as it shrinks, forming a crack. The cracks will be roughly hexagonal over the whole surface, though they vary quite a bit. It's the same principle as hexagonal cracks forming in mud where a puddle has just dried up. As the interior of the lava cools, the cracks deepen.

What are cobwebs?

Cobwebs are made from silk. The silk is spun, rather like toothpaste being squeezed out of a tube, through the end of the spider's abdomen. The silk is produced from special glands inside the spider – a female spider can produce seven different types of silk. Sometimes a spider will eat its old web and recycle the silk. Spider silk is incredibly strong – almost as strong as Kevlar, the material used to make bulletproof vests.

If the centre of the Earth is so hot, why isn't the ocean warmer?

You are right to say that the centre of the Earth is extremely hot – about 4,300°C. But it is a long way from the core to the surface, and the temperature falls the nearer to the surface you get. In fact, all things considered, the ocean is quite warm; while the Earth's crust can be quite cool if it isn't near a volcanic area.

If dark things absorb heat better than white, why do people in hot countries sometimes wear black clothes?

It is true that people who wear dark clothes in hot countries sometimes get hotter than if they wore white. However, as a result, the clothes are much hotter than the body, causing a large difference in temperature between the two.

Temperature differences cause air to move, creating a breeze. This cools the body. However, it is unlikely that this is the main reason why people in hot countries wear dark clothes. They are much more commonly worn for cultural reasons.

Does the speed of sound increase the further under water you go?

Sound is the transfer of vibrations from one particle to another. If sound is travelling through a material where the particles are close together, then not only will the sound travel further, it will also travel faster. So in water, which gets more dense the deeper you go, as more and more liquid presses down from above, sound will travel faster and further.

How does heat make things rise?

If you make any part of a liquid or a gas hotter than the air or liquid around it, then it will rise. This is because of density, which is worked out by dividing the mass of something by its volume. If a gas or a liquid is heated it becomes less dense. As atoms get more energy as you heat them, they move about more and start to take up more volume. So although the atoms have the same mass, the volume goes up, and so the density goes down. Things that are less dense than their surroundings rise. So balsa wood is less dense than water and floats, but it is more dense than air, so it doesn't fly away.

Why is a black surface more efficient at absorbing thermal radiation than any other coloured surface?

The simple answer is because it's black. Thermal radiation, such as light, is made up of many different wavelengths (which result in the colours of a rainbow, for example). When we perceive an object of a certain colour, say red, this is because the object is reflecting the particular wavelength of light that is the colour red; all the other wavelengths, and hence colours, are absorbed. A black object looks black because it reflects no energy, but absorbs it all.

Do stalactites have a transparent coating of crystals?

Transparent calcite crystals can coat the outside of a stalactite, and cause it to sparkle – which can give it the impression of being covered in crystals.

Is anything harder than diamond?

Diamond is still the hardest substance known to science. But American researchers say they have produced a composite material that contains crystals of carbon nitride, which scientists believe could be even harder.

The search for super-hard materials started in earnest in the late 1980s, when a formula was developed for calculating hardness. It showed, for example, that boron nitride, which was considered promising, could never be as hard as diamond. But the equation indicated that beta-carbon nitride (beta-C_3N_4) was a candidate.

Non-crystalline carbon nitride is easy to make in the lab, but the super-hard crystals proved difficult. "Left to themselves, carbon and nitrogen atoms simply don't want to form a crystal structure," says Yip-Wah Chung of Northwestern University in Evanston, Illinois, who led a team that claims to have made the crystalline form.

Chung joined forces with another Northwestern team led by Scott Barnett. The researchers made alternating thin layers of carbon nitride and titanium nitride using a process called magnetron sputtering, in which molecules of gas are fired at a solid target. The molecules knock atoms off the surface of the target, combine with them chemically, bounce off and are deposited on a nearby surface.

Chung's team fired nitrogen molecules at a target that was coated with carbon and titanium. The target rotated so that the nitrogen molecules hit the two materials alternately. As a result, successive layers of titanium nitride and carbon nitride were deposited on a surface held next to the target.

Titanium nitride and non-crystalline carbon nitride are both hard, but the composite material was twice as hard as either. Independent tests confirmed that the material was almost as hard as diamond. Then Chung found that the layers of carbon nitride seemed to contain crystals. Titanium nitride forms crystals easily, and Chung suggests that carbon nitride may somehow be forced to crystallise when sandwiched between layers of a titanium nitride crystal lattice.

Some researchers are sceptical of Chung's claim to have produced crystals of beta-carbon nitride. Even if he is correct, the crystals will have to be purified to produce a truly super-hard material. But such a material would have many uses. It could cut steel, which diamond cannot do because it burns when it gets hot. Mechanical parts coated with beta-carbon nitride would last much longer, and a thin layer could be used to protect computer discs.

Why does the grass look a lighter green at a distance? When you paint a landscape, you are told to paint the background lighter than the foreground because this is the way it looks in real life. Why?

There are lots of atmospheric effects near ground level that affect how we perceive things at a distance. The amount of dust in the air between you and the object increases with distance, and heat rising from the ground can change the refractive index of the air. These factors will tend to scatter and smear out the light you receive from an object. The further away the object is, the more the smudging will be evident.

Light from the sun is made up of all colours. Grass close to you will reflect green light, absorbing the

red and blue light. You see the grass as green. More distant grass will also reflect the same amount of green light, but dust in the atmosphere above it will reflect white light (all colours) towards you, too. This scattering of light dilutes the green you see from distant grass. The light you receive will be a faded (but still bright) version of the closer grass. This is most obvious in cities. If you look out of a tall building, distant buildings seem paler than closer ones. They will not, however, seem darker because lots of light is being reflected towards you, it's just that it is not all of a specific colour.

Is it true that the UK is tilted towards the south east?

Yes. The south east of the country is slowly sinking into the sea while the north west of Scotland is slowly rising, because of a process called isostatic compensation, whereby something that has been covered by a heavy weight bounces back when that weight is removed. Scotland used to be covered by ice during the last Ice Age.

How can plants take up water when gravity is pulling it down?

Water should indeed go "downhill" through the plant because of gravity. But things can be made to go against gravity if a big enough force can be put on them. In plants, the force is provided by the evaporation of water through pores. These pores are called stomata, and they are found on the underside of the leaves.

Water is "sucked up" through the plant in a conveyor-belt fashion. Water in the leaf veins moves into the air spaces to replace that lost through the stomata. Water in the stem replaces water that's just moved from the leaf vein. Water from the root replaces water just removed from the stem. Water from the soil replaces water that's just left the root. This movement of water through the plant is called transpiration.

Water can be moved along like this because its molecules are "sticky" – they cohere. That means if you move one molecule in a particular direction, you tend to also move many others behind it. There are other factors involved too, including the capillary uptake of water by the root hair cells.

Do tornadoes turn in opposite directions in the northern and southern hemispheres?

Tornadoes usually rotate anti-clockwise in the northern hemisphere and clockwise in the southern. They have been observed rotating "the wrong way" in either hemisphere, but this is less common. The effect of the Earth's rotation – known as the Coriolis effect – acts on objects moving with respect to the Earth's surface (aeroplanes, birds and so on). It is only significant over distances spanning hundreds or thousands of miles, and time spans of 12 hours or longer. Hence tornadoes themselves are not influenced by the Coriolis force. But the Coriolis force does affect violent storm systems called supercells, causing them to rotate in different directions in the hemispheres.

Many tornadoes arise from supercells, so the Coriolis effect indirectly causes the tornadoes to rotate differently in the two hemispheres.

It is not certain what causes "renegade" tornadoes to rotate in the other direction, but it may be something to do with the topography of the area they are in.

Why do we get more sunlight in the summer than in the winter?

Because the Earth is tilted, the northern hemisphere points more towards the Sun in the summer than in the winter. This means the Sun rises higher in the sky in summer, so our days are longer.

What makes a sea wave "break"?

In a sense, it trips over its own feet. Water waves move more slowly in shallow water than in deep water. This makes the bottom of a large wave travel more slowly than the top. Eventually the crest of the wave gets so far ahead of the water that is supporting it below that it falls over – so the wave breaks.

What causes earthquakes?

The Earth's crust is made up of 15 pieces or "plates". Currently, we think the plates float on the molten rock underneath and can move around. Earthquakes happen where the plates join – the fault lines – as the plates move and push against each other.

Clouds are made of tiny water droplets. So why are they white and opaque?

Clouds look white (or grey) because of the way light bounces around inside the water droplets. If light travelled straight through the cloud, it would be clear. These water droplets are the sort that form rainbows. Although the sky looks reasonably clear where a rainbow forms, there are in fact enough water drops to refract the light and create a rainbow.

However, in clouds the light is refracted and reflected in the droplets, making the ray bounce around inside the cloud before leaving. There is no coherency in the beam, so the white colour of the light is all that is left; rather like looking at a white wall as opposed to a mirror.

The droplets in storm clouds are larger and absorb and scatter more light, so storm clouds look darker. The thicker a cloud is the darker it appears, as it is more difficult for the sunlight to pass through.

Why is the outer skin of a cactus so fat?

The cactus is basically a big fat stem covered by a thick waxy cuticle. Because the cactus is naturally found in a dry habitat, conservation of water is vital. It has no leaves because they lose water too easily. The fact that they are thin and have a large surface area means evaporation takes place rapidly. The cactus uses its stem to perform the function of the leaves; that is to absorb sunlight and photosynthesise, making the plant's food. The thickness of the stem reduces water loss. The waxy cuticle that gives the plant its shiny appearance also prevents water loss.

What is the frequency of a rumble of thunder?

Every thunder rumble has a different frequency. The noise we hear as thunder is created when lightning superheats the air it travels through. When air is heated it expands and, in a lightning flash, the expansion is so fast that a shock wave is created, causing the sound wave we hear as thunder. Essentially, the frequency of the sound wave depends on just how fast the air expands, which in turn depends on the stability of the air and other complicated, thermodynamic factors.

But each roll of thunder sounds slightly different. You may have noticed that at the start of a roll of thunder you will hear a sharp clap and then the rest of the thunder rumble continuing after it. The sharp clap is a much higher frequency than the rumble.

The reason we hear different types of thunder – the long roll or the short crack – is due to the path the lightning takes.

Imagine a flash that starts a kilometre above our heads and travels diagonally to hit the Earth a kilometre from our feet. Every point on that path is (very roughly) the same distance from us, so the sound from every point of the flash hits us at about the same time. This gives a loud "crack" kind of noise. Now, imagine a flash that starts about a kilometre up but ends close to our feet. The sound from the start of the flash's path has to travel much further than the sound from the end and will, as a result, reach us much later. This creates the long, slow roll of thunder at a lower frequency.

In the northern hemisphere's winter the Earth is closer to the Sun – so why is it colder than summer?

Imagine a beam of sunshine as wide as the planet. When it reaches the planet some will strike the Earth full on, but as you go further North or South, the angle becomes more oblique. The more oblique that angle, the larger the area that that unit of the Sun's energy is spread around – which means those places will be less warm. The angle is most oblique at the poles, making them the coldest areas on Earth.

There are two complicating factors: the tilt of the Earth, and its very slightly elliptical orbit around the Sun – the earth is about 3 per cent closer to the Sun in January than in July. The planet is also tilted by roughly 23.5 degrees to the imaginary vertical line running from the North to the South Pole.

As we orbit, the direction in which this imaginary line is pointing changes very gradually, like a spinning top whose spoke is slightly off-vertical. This is called "precession"; the Earth's precession takes exactly a year, and

it is what causes the seasons.

As the Earth orbits the Sun, precession gradually changes the area which receives the most heat. Near the equator, there are no great seasonal differences in temperature, as the Sun's rays strike almost full-on all year round, resulting in a constantly high temperature.

The temperature is thus an interplay of two factors: our distance from the Sun, and which hemisphere is tilted towards it. Of the two, the tilting of the Earth – affecting the angle at which the Sun's rays hit the northern hemisphere – has a far greater effect on temperature than our varying distance from the Sun. So it's still cold in winter.

Where does geothermal energy come from?

Geothermal energy comes from many sources within the Earth. Initially, the Earth was one big ball of molten rock, formed by the gradual accretion of rock and dust. Some geothermal heat is produced because the rock is still cooling after that formation stage. But even after 4.6 billion years, the radioactive decay of minerals such as uranium still generates plenty of heat as well.

As ice is less dense than water, surely the sea level would fall if the ice caps melted?

Melting ice in the Arctic, which floats in the ocean, would not affect the sea levels. But most of the ice in the Antarctic is on top of a large piece of land; melting it would raise the sea level. The volume of ice in the Antarctic is 30 million cubic kilometres and accounts for more than 90 per cent of all fresh water on Earth. If this melted, sea levels would rise so much that Big Ben would be under water.

How do plants know what the seasons are?

Every plant has a biological clock that responds to temperature and light. With bulbs, small miniature plants with flowers develop within the bulb during the previous season (or in autumn, for spring blossoms). Each type of flower is programmed to start growing a specified number of months after the formation of this miniature plant (for example, tulips wait five months). After this wait, the bulb begins to let water enter the cells of the miniature plant. This makes the cells swell and elongate, so the flower, stem and leaves grow bigger until they are fully grown.

After the stem begins to grow, the growth rate depends on the temperature. If the weather is warm, the plant will grow faster and will bloom earlier.

What tells trees to shed their leaves for winter?

In many trees leaf fall seems to be brought about by shorter days and falling temperatures toward the end of the growing season.

Chlorophyll, the green pigment in plants, is lost; yellow and orange pigments called carotenoids become more conspicuous and, in some species, anthocyanin pigments accumulate. These changes cause the autumn colours of leaves.

There are some indications that day length triggers leaf loss in deciduous trees: some researchers think the lack of daylight breaks down a couple of plant hormones which are important in controlling leaf fall. Artificially increasing the level of two hormones, called gibberellins and auxins, in the autumn can halt leaf fall and preserve the leaves' greenness.

Why do plants such as hyacinths have such a strong scent? Is it because they are catering for dopey insects?

In wildflowers, scent is intended to attract pollinators. When plant selectors and breeders get involved, as with most or all of the garden forms, then colour, or scent, or shape, or doubleness of flowers often predominates. Scent sometimes "suffers" with selection for other features, and then breeders might try to bring strong scent back. The chemicals themselves in scent may not be attractive to us – some flowers attract flies for pollination, and some of those smell of rotting flesh or halitosis.

Why is the Earth's core solid when the surrounding medium is molten?

The Earth's core is solid because of "pressure freezing" – a process in which the pressure of the surrounding mass of material forces something that would otherwise be liquid to become solid. The first person to confirm that the

Earth had a solid core was Inge Lehmann, who died in 1993.

How do we know the age of the Earth?

The age of the Solar System is generally said to be about 4.6 billion years, but the age of the Earth is around 4.5 billion years as it took a bit of time for the planets to form once the Solar System had formed. The age of the Earth is calculated in a variety of ways. The minimum age of the Earth is given by the age of its oldest rocks – 3.8 billion years.

But erosion has removed some of the earliest rocks so we know it's older than that. By dating meteorites, which haven't changed much since the birth of the Solar System, we can constrain the maximum age of the Earth at 4.6 billion years. But it is the radioactive decay of certain minerals in the Earth which dates our planet more precisely – at about 4.5 billion years old.

The sea is made of rain; the rain is made from the sea – so where did the first raindrop come from?

When Earth first formed 4.5 billion years ago, much of its atmosphere was derived from volcanic out-gassings containing water vapour. This cooled and condensed to form drops of water – which would have collected in basins on the land, creating large lakes and oceans. So rain came before seas.

Another possibility is that the water on Earth came from a collision with a comet.

Why is the sea salty?

The early oceans were probably not salty. Erosion of local rocks, by rivers which flowed into them, provided the salts. All fresh water in rivers contains traces of salts and minerals, but these get concentrated in the oceans because they are left behind when water evaporates (to form clouds). This water falls as rain which eventually washes more minerals into the sea.

But if you measure the sea's salt content now, and work out how salty it should have been after billions of years of minerals being washed into it, it is much less salty than expected. Someone tried to calculate the age of the Earth from how salty the seas were and got a figure close to 5,000 years – so something else is happening.

Why is there a greater loss of ozone over the South Pole compared to the North Pole?

The increased ozone loss over the South Pole is due to the atmospheric conditions over the region. The large land mass of Antarctica sets up a polar vortex, which leads to a trapping of the chlorofluorocarbon molecules (CFCs) in that region of the atmosphere. When the southern polar spring comes and the sun shines again, the solar radiation breaks down the CFCs, releasing radicals (highly reactive atoms and molecules) that destroy the ozone. Hence the greatest ozone loss occurs in only a few weeks around the begining of the polar spring. Over the North Pole, such a vortex cannot occur as the land surface is too small; so there is not such a build-up of CFCs. The northern regions still suffer an ozone loss, but it is less dramatic.

Is it true that the temperature suddenly drops just after dawn?

It is true that the coldest time of day is just after dawn. During the night, the temperature steadily falls as the ground loses heat, which is not replaced by the Sun's rays. Even just after the Sun rises, the rate at which the ground loses heat is still greater than the rate at which the Sun is heating the ground, so the coldest time of day is just after sunrise.

How fast can volcanic lava flow?

The speed depends on the composition of the lava, the steepness of the hill it is flowing down, and how fast it is erupting. In general, lava flows faster the closer it is to the volcano and the nearer it is to the centre of the flow itself. The edges are more exposed to the air, and so they dry out more quickly.

How do we know what is inside the Earth?

It is not possible to go down far enough to reach the really interesting bits of the underworld because it gets too hot. To understand the centre of the Earth, the core, we have to use shock waves, like those that travel through the Earth after earthquakes. These show the different densities of the rocks below which gives us a clue to what they are.

Can volcanoes damage the ozone layer?

Yes, but it depends on the type of material extruded. The greater the quantity of gases capable of breaking down ozone, the greater the damage will be. Large volcanic eruptions produce a high column, transporting gases and particulate matter high into the atmosphere. Here it may linger for some time, and harm the ozone layer.

Did Pangaea break up into Gondwana and Laurasia, or did Gondwana and Laurasia join to form Pangaea?

Pangaea, Gondwana and Laurasia are all names given to ancient continents formed and destroyed according to the theory of plate tectonics. It is thought Pangaea broke up to form Gondwana and Laurasia.

Why do you get lines of flint in chalk cliffs?

Flints are made of an insoluble sort of silica (silicon dioxide in chemical terms), which is also sometimes called chert. Flint and chert commonly grow as lumps and nodules in limestones, and chalk is just a rather fine-grained, pure sort of limestone. The ground-waters present in buried rocks have a small amount of silica dissolved in them, which gets precipitated out as very fine crystals that amass in the lumps. The same ground-waters tend to dissolve holes in the chalk. Together, these processes mean that as fast as a bit of chalk is dissolved out, flint is deposited to fill the gap.

What is the ocean floor made of, and how thick is it?

The crust beneath the ocean differs from the crust beneath land in several ways: it is thinner, denser, younger and made in different ways. Both have rocks made up of the same minerals, just in slightly different proportions. The crust has silicon, aluminium, iron, magnesium, calcium, sodium and potassium oxides in it – just like any other rock. However, the oceanic crust is only about four miles thick.

What is the biggest volcano?

The island of Hawaii is probably the largest volcano on Earth. The distance from its base (on the floor of the Pacific Ocean) to the summit of Mauna Kea (about 13,000ft high) is some 30,000ft – greater than the height of Everest.

Do tectonic events on one side of the earth create geographical features on the other side?

Broadly, no. Seismic waves do travel through the earth's crust and mantle, often to great distances, but there is no evidence that they are strong enough to create a new geographical feature. Recent observational evidence also suggests this could not happen.

Earthquakes regularly occur at exactly the opposite side of the earth to seismic stations (for example in Tamanrasset, Africa and in Bogota, Colombia) but the instruments record no unusual ground motion. Since they are sensitive to displacements of the order of thousandths of a millimetre, there is no observational evidence that permanent features could be formed halfway round the earth.

What is a pingo?

A pingo is an ice-cored hill, typically conical in shape, growing and persisting only in permafrost. The word is of Inuit (Eskimo) origin and was first used by the botanist AE Porsild in 1938 to describe the ice-cored hills typical of the Mackenzie Delta in north-west Canada. Pingos range in height from a few to several tens of metres. The greatest concentration – about 1,450 of them – occurs in the Tuktoyaktuk area, east of the present Mackenzie Delta. Pingos grow through the force of the freezing of water, which is moving due to a pressure gradient to the site which becomes the pingo. Some types typically form in recently drained lake basins or channels.

Why are some clouds flat on top?

Cumulus clouds form when heat from the Earth (warmed by the Sun) causes convection in the lower atmosphere. The development and height of cumulus clouds will partly depend on the amount of convection, which is linked to the amount of heating. Strong convection leads to higher cloud tops.

Very often the atmosphere above the Earth will be layered and this means that winds may be stronger at greater altitudes. If the tops of a cumulus cloud reach a zone where wind speeds are greater than lower down, the tops can be sheared in the direction of the prevailing wind. This is called a castellate texture.

If the tide is said to be six metres high, what is that six metres measured from?

The six metres is the height of the tide above "Chart Datum", which is different for every port around the coast because of variations in the shape of the land, the depth of the sea, and so on. It is defined as being approximately the level of the Lowest Astronomical Tide, which is the lowest tide that can be predicted to occur under average meteorological conditions and under any combination of astronomical conditions.

This means that on rare occasions, when a particularly high tide is predicted to occur, the following low tide may be low enough to have a negative value.

Does geographical evidence support Milancovitch's theory on the ice ages?

Milancovitch suggested that there was and still is a cycle of ice ages and warmer climates. As a result, different layers of sediment would be laid down over history. There is some possible evidence in sediments for this theory of oscillating climates to hold true. Undoubtedly there are cycles of limestone, shale, sandstone and coal measures in Carboniferous and Jurassic rocks.

These changes in rock type represent changes in climate on a cyclical basis. There are even subtle changes in layers of chalk – which repeat themselves and could reflect climatic cycles.

But inferring rates of climatic change from rock types is very difficult and so far there is no conclusive geological proof of the Milancovitch theory.

Which way do the Earth's magnetic field lines go?

On a bar magnet, the field lines go from north to south, but the direction of the Earth's magnetic field goes from south to north. The problem arose because maps originally used the top of the Earth as north, and the bottom as south. Lodestones (naturally occurring magnets) were used as direction pointers, and it was a long time before physicists came up with bar magnets and theories for magnetism.

Unfortunately this mistake was not realised until it was too late to rectify, so the problem has stuck with us.

Where is the coldest place on Earth?

The South Pole is the coldest place on Earth, with average temperatures of -50°C (-58°F). The coldest place in Antarctica is the Russian station of Vostok, where temperatures as low as -89°C have been recorded.

Where is the highest waterfall in the world?

The Angel Falls in Venezuela are the highest falls in the world, at 979m (3,212ft).

What is the weight of Ayers Rock?

Ayers Rock, in the Australian outback, weighs about 10 million to 20 million metric tonnes – an estimate from its shape and density.

Of what material is Ayers Rock made?

Ayers Rock is a monolith of a terracotta-coloured arkose sandstone. Arkose is a term used to describe an arenaceous rock – that is one which is sandy or sand-like in appearance. There are three main groups of arenaceous rock: quartz sandstones, greywackes and arkoses. The definition of arkose is sandstone containing quartz and 25 per cent or more of feldspar.

I saw a rainbow very high in the sky near cirrus clouds, with no curve. It was on a damp evening. What was this?

What you saw was no rainbow – although it was very similar. Rainbows are caused by sunlight being reflected and split inside raindrops. This other effect is called parhelia, or sundogs. Instead of water, ice crystals (hexagonal in shape) refract light and refocus some of it towards you, giving a ring of light around the Sun.

It is rare to see the whole ring, but arc-sections are common. At the four compass points of this ring you often see brighter patches of "rainbow-like" light, several degrees in extent.

Why do the Earth's magnetic fields flip every million years or so?

The current understanding is that the Earth's magnetic fields are produced by a complex system of electric currents circulating in the molten part (not all of it is molten) of the Earth's iron core. The currents exist because molten iron is a good electrical conductor and is undergoing convective stirring as it passes its heat upwards into the overlying solid mantle.

The currents produce a magnetic field in a similar way to an electromagnet; but the whole thing is more complicated because the magnetic field interacts with the electric currents and keeps changing the convection pattern.

Inside the core the magnetic field is complicated but, fortunately, the net effect seen from the outside is less so, and the Earth's field we measure at the surface is rather like that from a bar magnet which is slowly wobbling. This is why the direction of magnetic north changes slowly with time.

It seems that the convection process sometimes gets into a pattern where the magnetic field seen from the outside becomes very small and then grows again but with the opposite polarity; that is, it reverses.

This has been shown to occur in some mathematical models of the Earth's core and also in physical models (involving complicated systems of bar magnets and coils of wire in the laboratory). The only problem is that we are not sure whether these models are exactly like what happens inside the Earth's core, so we cannot predict just what to look for when a reversal is imminent. The bottom line is that we understand the process in general, but not yet in extreme detail.

If the flip-over of the Earth's magnetic field is overdue, how long do you estimate it will be before it eventually happens?

Scientists believe that reversals of the Earth's magnetic field happen every 250,000 to 700,000 years. The time period over which this happens is thought to be around 5,000 years, although there is some evidence of previous reversals taking as little as 100 years.

During a reversal the magnetic field strength will decrease. If this decrease is significant, there could be an increase in the amount of radiation (solar wind – particles from the Sun) as these are usually deflected around the Earth by the magnetic field. Navigation by compass may also become more difficult.

The last magnetic polar reversal appears to have been 780,000 years ago, which could mean that we are indeed very overdue for one. However, scientists are currently trying to simulate the motion of the Earth's liquid core in an attempt to predict exactly what happens during field reversal.

The event does not seem to be very regular – as you can see from the range given above – and, since we are having a hard time trying to work out what exactly happens, accurately predicting the reversals is a long way away.

How heavy is the Earth's atmosphere?

Assuming the Earth to be a perfectly flat sphere with an air pressure of 9.65×10^4 newtons per square metre (14 pounds per square inch) all over its surface, the atmosphere weighs 4.9×10^{18} newtons (a mass of about 5 million billion tonnes).

Why do storm clouds tend to look darker than normal clouds?

Storm clouds have a lot of water in them in droplets that are larger than those in normal clouds. These larger droplets absorb and scatter more light than smaller ones, so the storm clouds look darker.

Is the ice crust on the polar seas made of falling snow? Also: at what temperature does the sea freeze? And are icebergs made of fresh water or of sea water?

Sea water is very cold and its freezing temperature depends on its salt content. Water gets less dense as it cools because of the bonding structure in the ice lattice pushing molecules further apart than they are when in a liquid state.

The sea freezes at about -2°C rather than 0°C owing to its salt content. Frozen icebergs, on the other hand, have virtually no salt in them. They are lumps of ice from the mainland glaciers that have formed from normal snow – that is, fresh water.

Icebergs made of salty water do exist, but they are rare.

Where are the worst levels of radon in the UK?

Radon is a radioactive gas produced naturally from granite rock which contains uranium. The international maximum safe dose of radon in the air is 200 becquerels per cubic metre, but exposure in some homes has been found to be well above 1,000 Bq. Some of the worst affected towns are Buxton in Derbyshire and Northampton and Kettering in Northamptonshire. In Devon, Cornwall and Northamptonshire, 24 percent of the homes tested were above the danger level.

Why is there more sodium than potassium in the sea when rocks contain as much potassium as sodium?

River beds and ocean floors contain a lot of clay, which is a fine-textured sedimentary deposit that is very good at absorbing potassium. It has spaces within its structure that suit the size and shape of the potassium minerals. In contrast, sodium does not get absorbed by the clay, so more of it is left in solution in the sea and rivers. Rocks on the sea bed that are essentially basalt are weathered just the same as those on land. When weathered, they produce clays which again absorb potassium, making it more scarce in seawater than sodium.

How is the Earth's magnetic field produced?

The current understanding is that the Earth's magnetic field is produced by a complex system of electric currents circulating in the molten part of the Earth's iron core – not all of which is molten. Because molten iron is a good electrical conductor, and the core is undergoing convective stirring (as its heat passes to the upper mantle), that generates currents.

Those currents produce a magnetic field just like a standard wire electromagnet, but the picture is complicated because the Earth's field interacts with the currents themselves, thus changing the convection pattern.

Inside the core, then, the magnetic field is extremely complicated, but fortunately the net effect seen from the outside is not so complicated. Measured at the surface, the Earth's field is rather like that from a slowly wobbling bar magnet. This is why the direction of magnetic north changes slowly with time.

How is ozone produced in the stratosphere?

First, molecular oxygen (consisting of two oxygen atoms joined by a covalent bond) is broken up by ultraviolet radiation. The individual oxygen atoms then combine with other oxygen molecules to form O_3.

If you go too high in the atmosphere, there are not enough molecules for the oxygen atoms to form ozone; too low, and there is not enough ultraviolet light to break up significant amounts of molecular oxygen, as reactions in the atmosphere above have absorbed it.

If the stratospheric "ozone layer" gets thinner, more ultraviolet light gets through to the ground, which is dangerous to life. At ground level, ozone is not useful: it is very chemically reactive and does not rise to the upper atmosphere as it reacts and produces more stable compounds long before reaching it.

On the shipping forecast they use the term "smoke". What does this mean?

"Smoke" is used to describe a certain condition of visibility. When visibility is low, you assume that something is in the air to cause it. When it's water drops, then that's called mist or fog; when it's drier, it's called haze. And there are two types of haze. Dust is the most common, but you also get smoke haze resulting from smoke itself or pollutants. Most UK stations don't report smoke unless they're 100 per cent certain that the cause is smoke; however, the station on the Isle of Man (Ronaldsway station), an independent station, does often report smoke.

Daily life

If you are in a sealed room with a light bulb and switch it off, why does it go dark? Does the light decay, or get absorbed by the walls? After all, if you look up at the night sky you can see the light from long-dead stars – why hasn't the light from them decayed?

Bulbs generate light from electricity through a thin metal filament, which heats and starts to glow. We see that glow as light. When you switch off a light, you stop the electricity passing through the filament. It is not that the light has decayed, it is just not being produced anymore, and any that was produced will have been absorbed. This happens almost instantaneously.

By contrast, even the nearest stars are about four light years away. If a star was extinguished now, we would still see its light for the next four years. The more distant the star, the longer its light takes to travel to us. The light doesn't decay, it takes a finite time to travel large distances.

Is it true that you should turn mobile phones off when in petrol stations because they spark and are therefore fire risks?

Yes, but not because they spark. Mobile phone signals can interfere with electronic equipment; this is well known in hospitals, where mobiles can disrupt patients' automatic drips. The same applies to petrol stations; you could end up paying £130 for £20 of petrol, or the signals could interfere with sprinkler systems if there were a fire. So, no electronic equipment should be used in petrol stations, as the electronics could go wrong and present a fire hazard.

Is it harmful to swallow chewing gum? Can it get "tangled up" in your intestine?

No – this is an apocryphal tale, probably started by parents to stop children chewing gum. It is not digestible but does not attach to stomach walls – quite the opposite: it cannot stick to the moist, slippery walls of the intestines, and so will pass straight through.

How is "non-stick" Teflon stuck on to frying pans?

The surface of a pan that is to be coated with Teflon is quite rough. Up close, you'd probably see something like the surface of a tarmac road – lots of cracks and lines. When the Teflon is poured on to this surface it fills these cracks.

As it solidifies, it gets caught in the cracks, and thus forms a bond with the surface of the pan. So although Teflon is very smooth when it's solid, when it's a liquid it can flow and fill surface cracks so that it can't be pulled off.

Why does alcohol make you drunk?

Alcohol is a depressant. It inhibits central nervous system receptors, which makes it difficult to control your body. In effect, it does the same as an anaesthetic, but not as severely.

What is the air pressure inside a soap bubble?

The pressure inside the bubble is greater than the pressure outside by an amount which is twice the surface tension (the force between the molecules making the skin) divided by the bubble's radius. This difference in pressure tends to split the bubble apart. But what really makes bubbles pop is that there is a small amount of water trapped in the film, and this tends to drain to the bottom of the bubble under gravity. Eventually the weight of this region of water becomes too heavy for surface tension to support, and the film begins to split. The difference in pressure makes the split grow, and pop!

If you half-fill a bottle with hot water, put your hand over the top and shake, a build up of pressure can be felt. Why?

The hot water in the bottle is heating the cold air, which makes it expand. Shaking heats the air further and increases the surface area of the water from which water molecules can evaporate.

This increases the number of atoms and molecules in the available space and thus increases the pressure.

How does a radiator work?

Radiators heat the air around them, which then rises because hot air expands and is therefore less dense than the air around it. This leaves a gap into which the cold air in the room can flow. Cold air near the radiator then heats up and again moves out of the way. This cycle keeps going until (theoretically) the air in the room is all at the temperature of the radiator.

How do light bulbs work?

A light bulb contains a thin wire filament. When a current flows through this filament the metal heats up and then glows, giving out light. As the inside of the light bulb is a vacuum, there's no oxygen to oxidise the filament so it lasts a long time.

How do plasma balls work?

The small metal ball in the centre of the big glass one is charged up to a high voltage so when the outer glass sphere is earthed, by touching it for example, a plume of charge, or spark, jumps across. The sphere is filled with a low pressure mixture of inert gases, mainly nitrogen. The light of the spark is produced by ionisation of the gas; gas electrons are knocked off the gas atoms and as they re-combine they emit light.

How does a tyre pressure gauge work?

A tyre pressure gauge is like a syringe with a valve on the end where the needle would be. There's also a spring holding the inside and outside of the "syringe" together. The air in the tyre is under such pressure that it forces air inside the syringe through the one-way valve. The air can't get out again until the gauge is removed from the tyre. This air forces the inside of the gauge to move out.

But the spring tries to stop the inside moving. Eventually the pull from the spring is sufficient to balance the push from the air and the inside stops. This is the point at which the tyre pressure is shown on a scale along the side of the gauge.

Does a hot drink give you more energy than a cold drink (of the same liquid)?

In theory, yes. One kilogram of water absorbs about 4,200 Joules (equivalent to 1 kilocalorie) for every increase of one degree Celsius in temperature. Nevertheless, if you raise your temperature above its normal level, the body uses energy in an attempt to return to normal.

However, if your body was below its normal temperature (for example, you may be suffering from hypothermia) then a hot drink will go some way to warming you up. Since the drink partly does the work of warming you up, less energy has to leave the body so, in effect, the drink has given you more energy.

Why does a hot chip pan erupt when cold water is poured on top?

Hot oil in a pan has a temperature well above 100°C, the boiling point of water. If you pour water into the pan it tries to sink under the oil, and gets mixed in with it. Besides this mixing, the water is heated rapidly and starts to turn to steam. Being a hot gas, the steam tends to rise and expand: any oil on top of it will get pushed up in the eruption.

This produces a cloud of oily droplets which bursts into flame when it comes into contact with the gas flame or electric element in the cooker. That is why it is always useful to have a non-water fire extinguisher in your kitchen.

Why does sherbet fizz?

The "fizzy" feeling on your tongue is a mild pain response. Sherbet and fizzy drinks cause fizzing in similar ways. In fizzy drinks, the carbon dioxide in the bubbles is converted by an enzyme in saliva to carbonic acid, a weak acid that irritates the tongue. Sherbet contains citric acid and tartaric acid, which irritate the tongue in the same way.

Before I go to bed, I get a fresh glass of water. In the morning, it's full of air bubbles. Why?

Overnight the water slowly warms up to room temperature and any gas dissolved in it becomes less soluble. As the gas comes out of solution some of the bubbles formed will have enough buoyancy to rise to the surface while others will cling to the inside of the glass. How does the gas get there in the first place? Well, all water contains small amounts of dissolved gases.

You can see the whole effect happening more quickly when you boil water. Before the water actually starts to boil, bubbles appear on the side of the pan. These are the dissolved gases coming out of solution.

Why do onions give you bad breath?

Because of the chemicals inside the cells of the onion. These are released when we chop the onion

(we smell them) and when we chew it. Once it is in the stomach, our bodies break the onion into even smaller pieces. All of these processes release the chemicals inside the onion cells. Some are gases, so they are expelled back into the mouth from the stomach, often in the form of a belch. The bad breath is simply the presence of onion gases in the mouth and throat; it goes once the onion has been properly digested.

Why does tilting the tag on a rear-view mirror reduce the glare, and yet still produce an image?

Mirrors are silvered on the back of the glass, which is where most of the light is reflected from; but some light (about 5 per cent) is reflected from the front. On a normal mirror, the front and back sides are parallel, so you don't really notice this effect. Rear-view mirrors are wedge-shaped, so the two reflections come back at different angles.

During the day, the reflection you see comes from the efficient silvered back of the glass. At night, when you flick the tag, the mirror moves and you only see the weak reflection from the front of the glass. This reduces the glare.

When we use a straw to suck water from a glass, what is actually happening?

This is all to do with air pressure. We have to think about the pressure in two places, first the pressure of air inside the straw, and also the air pressure outside, which is pressing down on the surface of

49

the water in the glass. When you suck with your mouth, you remove some of the air from the inside of the straw. This means that the air pressure inside the straw is less than the air pressure outside. This difference in pressure means that air from outside tries to get inside the straw to even out the difference. As the air tries to get in, it pushes the water ahead of it, and hence up the straw.

It sounds odd, but when you suck water through a straw, it is actually being pushed from underneath, rather than being sucked from above.

At what altitude does the cabin of a passenger aircraft begin to become pressurised, and at what altitude does the pressure-level become stabilised? Also, is it just the cabin that gets pressurised, or the cargo holds, too?

As soon as the engines are on, the aircraft becomes pressurised. Before you take off, the pressure in the cabin is more than atmospheric. When the plane takes off, it rises about 90m a minute, up to about 9,000m. While the aircraft ascends, the pressure decreases outside it and also, at a slower rate, inside. The pressure-level stabilises when the plane remains at a certain altitude. At 9,000m, the most common flying-altitude, the pressure inside is what it would be outside at 2,000-2,500m. That may seem high, but several villages in the Alps are higher, and you don't get serious respiratory problems below 3,500m.

How high the aircraft can go is limited by the pressure differential between the outside and inside.

The pressure inside the plane is greater than outside, so the air inside is pushing against the walls, trying to expand. That exerts pressure on the joints of the aircraft: the greater the difference in pressure, the greater the stress.

The cargo holds are pressurised as well as the cabin. The only two parts of the plane that are not pressurised are the undercarriage, where the wheels go, and a back compartment containing the flight-data recorders.

When David Beckham takes a free kick, he kicks the right-hand side of the ball. The ball spins anti-clockwise and curls to the left as it travels. Given that the air will be travelling over the right hand side of the ball faster than the left, why doesn't the ball curve to the right due to the lower pressure produced?

Because the ball is spinning on itself, the air on one side of the ball is moving past it faster than the other side. Let us assume that we are looking at the ball from above as it flies through the air. The ball spins anti-clockwise, so relative to the ball, its right-hand side (RHS) is moving towards the front of the ball, while its left-hand side (LHS) is moving towards the back of the ball. This actually means that the air flow on the RHS is slowed down at the surface of the ball, due to greater friction.

On the other hand, the air flow on the LHS is speeded up. This is the source of the force. The very same that allows planes to fly. When air moves slightly faster, the space between molecules is very slightly increased; this means a decrease in the pressure at that point. A decrease in pressure is equivalent to a sucking force. Hence, the LHS experiences a sucking force.

Similarly, when the air is slowed down on the RHS, an increase in pressure results in a pushing force. Overall, the ball will start to swerve towards the LHS. If you kick the ball with the inside of the left foot, the ball spins clockwise, and the ball this time swerves to the RHS. If you increase the spin on the ball, the force will increase.

Can a household lightbulb be run off normal batteries? If so, how many?

A desklamp may have a 60W bulb that runs off 240V mains. (W = watts, the unit of power; V = volts, the unit of voltage.) The current would be 0.25 A (amps). This is calculated by dividing the power by the voltage.

Batteries have different voltage ratings, so the number needed to try to light a desklamp would be affected by the voltage of each battery (or strictly speaking, cell). The lower the voltage of each cell, the more would be needed. If we assume each cell is rated 1.5V, you would need 60 of them connected in series (all in a line) to supply the required 240V.

There is a catch to this simple calculation. The current supplied may not be sufficient to light the bulb to normal brightness. This is because the more cells you use, the more resistance there is in the circuit, and this reduces the current that can be drawn.

For practical reasons as well, the more connections there are in the circuit, the more chance there is of a connection not being sound, and so either making a gap in the circuit that current can't flow past, or at the least, will introduce a large resistance that will make it difficult for current to flow. Finally, using batteries is massively more expensive than using mains electricity.

What happens to the candle wax when a candle burns? Where does it go?

Candle wax is the fuel which is burnt to keep the candle going. When you light a candle, the flame melts the wax at the top of the candle into liquid form. This liquid travels up the wick via capillary action and is transformed into a gas by the heat of the flame. This gas combines with oxygen in the air, giving out the heat and light that you see as a flame. Candle wax is a mixture of chemicals, which contain carbon, nitrogen, oxygen and hydrogen. When combined with the oxygen in the air, new chemicals are created. These are gases – carbon dioxide, nitrogen, and water vapour – which float into the atmosphere, so you can't see where the wax has gone.

How does polish, such as Mr Sheen, prevent dust from sticking to objects?

There are many different types of antistatic spray on the market. They form a protective layer so that things that were previously insulators can now carry a small amount of charge. Dust, which will either have an extra electron or be missing some electrons, will be charged. Charged things are attracted to other charged things – like the screen of a television or computer. The dust then is likely to stick to it. These sprays allow electrons to either flow into the dust or away from the dust and so the dust returns to a neutral state. This dust then won't stick to charged objects like the screen and will fall to the floor under the pull of gravity.

Why don't today's railway lines have expansion gaps as they used to? How come they don't distort with variations in temperature?

Modern railway lines are laid down under tension (ie they are stretched). A rise in temperature just serves to decrease the tension. Continuously welded rails have the advantage that they give passengers a smoother ride (less "clickety clack"), and they also require less maintenance. Where expansion gaps are still used, the gaps are not butt-jointed, rather the ends of the rails are tapered, so they slide relative to each other, but no gap appears.

Why do frozen peas rotate and go up and down in a fizzy drink?

"Carbonated drinks" fizz because they have carbon dioxide gas dissolved in them. When you pour the drink into a glass the gas slowly comes out of solution and forms bubbles that rise to the surface as fizz. The tiny bumps and scratches all over the surface of the glass are good at allowing these bubbles to form, which is why most of the lines of fizz seem to be coming from the bottom and sides of the glass. Frozen peas, or in fact any object with a rough surface, that are dropped into the drink also allow bubbles to form, which may stay attached to the pea. All these bubbles of gas on the pea make it float to the surface. Now the gas can escape however, so the pea becomes heavier than water and sinks again. If more bubbles form on one side of the pea than the other then it will be forced to rotate as well as float to the surface.

Can stainless steel rust?

Some stainless steels will rust, especially cheaper grades. Sometimes makers try to pass off chromium alloy steels as stainless steels (technically, steel has to have at least 11 per cent chromium to be "stainless"). Essentially, new stainless steel forms a thin surface layer of oxide, which is transparent and prevents further decay. If this layer is eroded or compromised, corrosion will occur. No grade is totally immune to all chemicals, although the more expensive grades remain shiny while becoming pitted over time.

Why when I pour a fizzy drink does a stream of bubbles appear to come from one bubble that remains fixed to the glass?

The bubbles in fizzy drinks are undissolved carbon dioxide, which is also present in drinks as a dissolved gas. The gas bubbles form more easily on slightly rough, slightly porous places, so it may be that the points from which the bubbles rise are where the surface of your glass is less smooth. This is a trick known by the makers of beer glasses – sometimes you get glasses with pictures etched on the bottom, so the bubbles form there, and the "head" of the beer lasts longer. In Germany, they put rice grains in the bottom of the glass so more bubbles form and the drink doesn't go flat.

Is it possible to "unshrink" a wool garment that has been shrunk in the tumble-drier?

Sorry, no. But you might want to know why shrinking happens in the first place...

Two conditions are required for wool to shrink: water and heat. The outside of the wool fibre is hydrophobic (it repels water). The inside of the wool fibre is hollow, and hydrophilic (it absorbs water). Even though wool wants to repel water around the fibre, at a certain point of getting wet it reverses its process of repelling water to one of absorbing water. When this happens, it brings water into its core and holds it.

At the microscopic level, the outside of the wool fibres look as if they are made from overlapping filaments – a bit like tiles on the roof of your house. When wool gets wet and heat and agitation are present, these filaments have a tendency to overlap and lock together. Result: the wool shrinks.

The only way to avoid shrinking is to let wool dry in a cool area, and block or stretch out the fibres when the fabric is still wet. Dry-cleaning is the surest means of cleaning without shrinking. You can hand wash, but the clothing must be cared for properly. The only way you can safely wash wool is if it has been chemically treated to "descale" the fibre.

Why does cold water sputter and fizz when sprayed on a very hot surface?

Normally, water will boil at 100°C. If the temperature of the surface is much greater than that, the water will "evaporate", in other words boil, very rapidly. This evaporating water forms a cushion of air that the blobs of water can float around on. As they float around, more and more of their water evaporates and replaces the cushion of air that is gradually lost. This in turn creates a large amount of turbulence underneath the blob of water and it is this turbulence that sends it speeding all over the tin plate.

How do damp clothes dry at room temperature?

Water molecules on the clothes are attracted to other water molecules and also to the molecules that make up the clothing. Each water molecule finds itself in a "sticky" environment, which makes it hard for it to escape into the air, but it does have enough energy to move, swapping positions with other water molecules.

Heat can be thought of as energy that molecules possess. The more heat, the greater the amount of energy they have, and the easier they find it to overcome the stickiness of their surroundings.

Temperature is a measure of the average energy that the molecules possess, but a few will have less, and a few more than the average. At a room temperature of 20°C, some water molecules will have enough energy to overcome the forces from the other molecules, and will be able to escape from the clothes into the air. As this process continues there will be less and less water on the clothes, until eventually they are dry.

If the temperature is higher than 20°C, more molecules will have enough energy to evaporate, and the clothes will dry more quickly. Some of the water molecules that have escaped into the air may fall back on to the clothes and get stuck again. Putting clothes out on a windy day speeds up the drying process, because the wind blows away the water molecules that have escaped, so they are less likely to get stuck again.

How do the metal trays that defrost frozen meat work? They are not heated, yet at room temperature they defrost in minutes.

A normal dish does not conduct heat very well because it is a good insulator, unlike metal. A metal tray will soon lose any heat it has to the frozen meat. The metal might even be cold but it will nevertheless conduct heat from the surrounding air into the meat.

These days bread isn't just made of flour and water. What else is added?

Bakers often add their own mix of wheat and other grains to give the bread texture and flavour. Some add vitamins. In 1986 the manufacturers of the flour and wheat mixes also added a compound called creta preparate to some vitamin-enhanced breads, as a source of calcium and as a filler.

How do colour photocopiers work?

The image is scanned four times – once for each of the three primary printing colours (cyan, magenta and yellow) and once for black. Using charge-coupled devices, or CCDs, which are electrical sensors that react very precisely to light, the copier assesses the brightness of the image for each colour. The paper then rolls around the drum four times as the correct amount of each coloured ink is applied.

In an aeroplane at 30,000ft, you can often see water droplets, even though the temperature is below freezing point. How can this be?

Water can exist as a liquid below 0°C, and often does. There are two main reasons. Impurities in water reduce its freezing temperature, which is why salt is put on roads in winter. Adding salt can lower the freezing point as far as -13°C. Pure liquid water can also exist below 0°C. For water to freeze, molecules must form the correct structure. A container, such as a cup or bowl, offers plenty of chances for this structure to form. With a small amount of water, the structure is less likely. Hence drops of liquid water can exist in the atmosphere at temperatures as low as -40°C.

How can artificial sweeteners taste like sugar yet contain no calories?

Sugar is very sweet and has a high energy content, or calorific value. But sweetness and calorie content aren't necessarily linked. Sweetness – which is a difficult property to measure, unlike calories – appears to be caused by a different chemistry to calorie content. In fact, we can record sweetness only through taste tests.

But chemical structure and sweetness do appear to be linked. Most sweet compounds seem to have a chemical structure known as "AH.B", where A and B are negative atoms, which are thought to form bonds with a protein in our sweet-sensitive taste buds. To do this effectively, A and B must be around 0.3 nanometres (billionths of a metre) apart. This is a property seen in sucrose, glucose, saccharin and aspartame.

How do metal detectors work?

To sniff out metallic objects, they all rely on a metallic "search" coil (sometimes called a search loop) with an alternating current running through it. The AC causes a uniform alternating electromagnetic field around the coil. But when that field passes over a metallic object, it induces tiny currents – called eddy currents – in the object. That weakens and distorts the detector's field (because the eddy current comes from the field's energy). When the field passes over a magnetic material (say, iron or magnetite) it strengthens the field. An audible note linked to the energy in the coil then alerts you when the search loop passes over a conducting metallic object (less energy) or a magnetic material (more energy). Thus you can also distinguish between metallic and magnetic objects.

When a person is floating (eg, in a swimming bath) and tenses their muscles, the body begins to sink. Why?

The only factor that will affect buoyancy is the weight (or amount) of air in the person under water – inhalation makes you go up and exhalation makes you go down. This is standard practice in diving. Tensing your muscles without breathing will not affect your buoyancy *per se*, though it might perhaps change your centre of buoyancy (ie, by moving your diaphragm), resulting in a small displacement. Or you might unconsciously tense one set of muscles slightly more than another – which would affect your orientation in the water, and so possibly your position. Or by tensing your muscles, you might actually move your arms and legs, albeit slightly and without your knowledge. This would change the relative positions of your centre of gravity and centre of buoyancy, causing a small change in position.

However, all the movements described above would be slight, and they would certainly not cause you to sink. Experts at the National Sports Medical Institute and several diving schools agree: it simply doesn't happen. So they wonder – are you sure you aren't breathing out when you tense your muscles?

Why does newspaper go yellow faster than other paper?

The main components of wood are cellulose and lignin. Cellulose is long-fibred and strong – so paper remains supple over a long time. Lignin is a polymer that makes wood hard, and is acidic. When making high-quality paper, the pulp is cooked, which removes the lignin. However, the newspaper publishers' main concern is to get the news to the reader as quickly and as cheaply as possible. Thus they use the cheapest papers and the cheapest inks. As newspapers have a very short shelf life, there isn't much point in making them out of posh paper. Newspaper is made from wood that hasn't been cooked, so most of the lignin remains. This is what turns yellow on exposure to sunlight.

Why doesn't dew form on a car parked in a car port, although it is open on all sides?

This is because of heat loss. The car port is insulated by the roof both from excessive heat build-up during the day, and from sudden heat loss at night. So during the day, moisture-heavy air doesn't collect under the port because the air there is cooler than that around it (and so can't absorb as much moisture as warm air). At night, when the earth starts to lose heat, the car port stays at relatively the same temperature as before; so there isn't such a sharp drop in temperature, nor so much moisture in the air there. The result: dew doesn't form.

Why does jelly set when you put tinned pineapples in it, but does not set when you put fresh pineapple in it?

Raw pineapples, like figs and papayas, contain an enzyme (known as a protease) that breaks proteins down into small fragments. If raw pineapple is put in gelatin for a dessert or fruit salad, this enzyme digests the gelatin molecules and liquefies the water-protein gel. Canned pineapple has been heated, which deactivates the enzyme, and so it co-operates quite well with gelatin.

What makes the white trails which are left behind when a plane has passed overhead?

One reason is that water vapour from the plane's exhaust freezes in the cold air to make ice particles. Also, as air passes over the plane's wings and tail, its pressure drops, causing it to cool rapidly, which condenses any water vapour. Concorde also creates strange air and water patterns on take-off and landing: a mist often forms over the top of the wings as the lower-pressure air just above them is less able to hold water than air underneath.

Why doesn't the chocolate in chocolate chip cookies melt when they're being cooked?

To all intents and purposes, it does, but it is held in place by the dough around it. However, the chocolate doesn't melt as much as ordinary chocolate would, because it has been tempered. Tempering is the process where chocolate is repeatedly heated and cooled until a crystal-like structure appears within it. This makes the chocolate more stable and gives it a glossy shine and a crispy surface.

Why is it dangerous to burn many fuels in a limited air supply?

Insufficient air means alkanes and other carbon-based fuels burn to give carbon monoxide and carbon (soot) instead of carbon dioxide. This is called incomplete combustion.

Carbon monoxide is poisonous, and is responsible for many accidental deaths.

Gas fires that haven't been serviced regularly can burn gas incompletely. In a poorly ventilated room, the build-up of carbon monoxide can put the occupants into a coma, and kill them if they are not found.

Carbon monoxide detectors are available, which, like smoke detectors, make a loud bleeping noise.

Why does electricity like to go to earth?

The flow of electricity is a result of what is known as a potential difference. This is like a pressure difference in a water pipe. If you fix a hosepipe to a tap and turn the water on, the water flows because there's water pressure at the tap that forces the water through the pipe – but if the hose end is closed, it won't flow. Electricity is the same. Electrons at one end of the wire have energy, while those at the other end connected to earth haven't. This creates a sort of "energy pressure" that forces the energy along the wire. Of course, for the purposes of an electrical circuit, "earth" can be defined as a point in the system with a lower potential than any other. The electrons then flow to that.

Why do blades in razors, which are many times harder than the materials they are designed to cut, become blunt?

The fact that steel is much stronger than hair is largely irrelevant; water is much "softer" than rock, yet most of the Earth's surface has been moulded by the action of water. A blade is thin. The thinner the blade and the more regular the edge, the sharper the cut and the more often it has to be sharpened to maintain that sharpness. As the blade passes over the stubble on a person's chin, the hair knocks off individual atoms from the edge of the steel blade. As there are many thousands of hairs, it doesn't take long to dull the blade slightly. When we consider a blade to be dull, it has not really lost that much of its edge. Even if each hair only removes one atom, the blade can be dulled quickly.

Why does it always take longer to fly from east to west than from west to east?

Because of the wind. Winds in the upper atmosphere always flow from west to east. If you are flying from east to west, you have to fly against the prevailing wind, which means the journey takes longer.

What happens to waste from aeroplane toilets?

It's a myth that it can leak out and fall to the ground in huge frozen blocks. Waste on aircraft is stored in tanks, which are pumped out later on the ground. The bits of ice which can fall from a plane generally come from the wings, where ice accumulates from water vapour in the clouds.

How do they put stripes in toothpaste?

Basic toothpaste is white. Coloured gels are then made in separate steel mixers, and each colour is piped to a specially designed nozzle which keeps the colours separate as they are pumped into the tubes – which are filled from the bottom up at a rate of about 250 per minute, and sealed. The stripes are carefully formulated to be stiff enough not to flow into a single messy mix, yet

soft enough to be squeezed out of the nozzle. Because each tube is filled to capacity, the colours can't normally mix up.

Why do we crave chocolate?

Chocolate contains large amounts of phenylethylamine, which is also present in our bodies and released during sexual arousal, heightening sensation and raising the heart rate. It also contains methylxantine and theobromine, which have similar effects to caffeine. And if that isn't enough, it is solid at room temperature but melts at just below body temperature – that is, in your mouth.

How does a lie detector work?

Lie detectors work on the principle that anyone who's lying will be nervous, and nervous people tend to produce more adrenaline, which makes their hearts beat faster, their skin temperature rise and makes them sweat more. A lie detector basically measures how these things change during questioning. However, people generally get nervous anyway if they're being questioned, while some people can control their heart rate if they concentrate. So, lie detectors aren't foolproof indicators of guilt.

What causes car sickness?

Car movement is noticed by a part of your body called the inner ear. In your inner ear are three curved tubes called semi-circular canals. If you are reading a book or looking at the inside of the car your eyes tell your brain that you are not moving but the little tubes in your ear (the semi-circular canals) tell your brain that you are moving. This confuses the brain and makes you feel sick. If you look out of the window of the car and watch things moving past you will make your eyes realise that you are moving and you won't feel so ill.

Some microwave food containers seem to have metallic films on top of them. Isn't that dangerous, because metal things in microwaves cause sparks?

Metal containers can produce dangerous arcing in a microwave oven. However, many food packages actually contain thin films of metal that speed the cooking process. For example, new packaging techniques use polyethylene terephthalate (PET) film laminated to paperboard as a "heat susceptor" – a metallised film that absorbs microwaves, and becomes a miniature frying pan to brown or fry the foods in the package.

So yes, metal in sufficient thicknesses can cause sparking. But thin films can improve the cooking ability of the microwave.

If you've got ice cubes in a glass of water, what happens to the level of water when they melt?

The water level stays the same. The amount of space the ice cube takes up in the water is exactly the same size as the water it makes when it melts, even though some of the ice cube sticks up out of the

water. This is because water shrinks when it melts and expands when it freezes, so the amount that's sticking above the water indicates the extent that the frozen water has expanded.

This, incidentally, is why the threat of sea-level rise from global warming is not due to melting icebergs. It's due to the melting of ice which presently lies on land.

When you defrost something in a plastic container in a microwave, you often end up with a collapsed container – as if something had sucked the sides in. Why?

As you defrost things, the water on the surface escapes into the air in the container. A lot of this water will escape as superheated steam from the container, through the tiniest pores in the seal of the lid.

But because these containers are designed to keep food fresh by keeping out bacteria, no air can get back in to fill the space left by the departing water. This means the air pressure inside the container is less than that outside, so the sides of the container cave inwards.

If you put a cup of water and a cup of maple syrup in the microwave at the same time, and for the same length of time, why does the maple syrup get hotter?

Two things affect how fast a material heats up in a microwave: its heat capacity and its radiation density. The heat capacity is defined as the amount of energy required to make a specific amount of the material rise in temperature by one degree Centigrade.

Assuming the microwave spreads its energy equally to two equally filled cups, the syrup must have a lower heat capacity than water, since it's warmer. That's not a safe assumption, though. Microwave ovens don't impart a one-off blast of energy to food – so the radiation density of the material also matters.

A microwave oven works by emitting high-energy waves inside its cooking space. The waves bounce off the walls, and sometimes hit the food. If they come in contact with the food, some waves will be reflected and some will pass into the material. Inside the food, the microwaves lose energy, due to the presence of the material. The wave loses energy due to the contact with the material: some energy is translated into heat in the material. If some of the wave's energy passes through the material it behaves like the other waves, bouncing off the walls again until it hits food again and loses some more energy, until it is completely gone.

Now imagine you are swimming through water, and then through syrup. You will lose much more energy swimming through the syrup than the water. The energy you lose has to go somewhere – specifically, to the material you are swimming through. Swim equal distances through the water and the syrup, and the syrup ends up warmer.

If we assume the waves are equally distributed through the microwave oven, the waves will travel the same distance through the water as the syrup, but losing

more energy to the syrup – which ends up hotter.

Is it true that swimming pool water can make bleached hair go green?

Yes, it is possible. The peroxide used to bleach hair damages it, which makes it more susceptible to collecting impurities such as iron and copper ions from the water. These ions can cause discoloration of the hair.

How is ovenproof glass made?

To make glass tough enough to withstand the high temperatures in cookers, a chemical called boron oxide is added. This also makes the glass resistant to fast temperature changes.

How are plastic bags made?

All plastic bags and sacks are made by a process know as "blown film extrusion" in which the molten plastic is blown up like a balloon as it is stretched out to produce a continuous tube of the film. This film is flattened to make a continuous double layer – which is what makes new bags difficult to open sometimes. This is then printed, cut to the appropriate length and sealed, and a handle is cut out, all in one process which is continuously repeated to produce individual bags.

How do things rust?

To create rust you need water, air and (of course) iron. The reaction is complicated, but essentially the oxygen reacts with the iron, with the help of the water, to make a reddish compound called iron oxide. Be wary of "rustproof" treatments which challenge you to "paint a nail with this and then put it in a jar of water – it won't rust!" If you do this, try immersing an untreated nail too – that probably won't rust either.

Why are grandfather clocks so tall?

The longer the pendulum, the longer the swing. To take one second to swing from one side to the other and one second to swing back, a pendulum needs to be almost exactly one metre long – a remarkable coincidence of natural ratios between the Earth's gravity and *pi*, the circular ratio.

How much vitamin C is found in pure orange juice?

A litre of orange juice contains about 300 milligrams of vitamin C, which is five times the recommended daily dose for adults.

Why does metal feel colder to the touch than plastic when they are both at room temperature?

Your body temperature is about 37° Celsius, and room temperature is about 20°C to 25°C. This means heat from your body is transported to objects you touch. Metal conducts heat better than plastic, so it conducts that heat away from you into the metal more quickly than plastic does. If both materials were at body temperature (or

rather, skin temperature) you would probably not feel a difference, since no heat would be transferred.

Are luminous watch faces dangerous?

Not now. But about 40 to 45 years ago it was common to use radioactive radium paint to make parts of wrist watch dials luminous. This posed a health hazard – particularly to the dial painters, many of whom developed cancers. The watch industry eventually acknowledged the hazards, and so turned to tritium (radioactive hydrogen) and phosphor paints for luminescence.

This technology is still used by some watchmakers, though a better technology now uses tritium gas enclosed in glass vials, which excite or activate a phosphor coating to provide a self-illumination. This minimises any hazard, since the tritium gas cannot penetrate the glass vial; if a vial is broken, the gas simply dissipates into the atmosphere.

What are cellophane and Sellotape made of, and do they decompose?

Sellotape and cellophane are made from natural cellulose which comes from soft woods. They will degrade, but not all that readily. Factors such as temperature, humidity, acidity and microbial activity control how fast they degrade outside. In a tropical rainforest Sellotape will degrade within months. In a British compost heap it could take years.

In Britain, we can now buy gas from a variety of companies, but it all comes down the same pipes. How do the companies know how much to bill you?

The gas meter at your house registers how much gas you use, but not who supplies it. But this doesn't really matter. You have a contract with a certain gas company – the "provider" – that says you'll pay them for the gas you use. The provider has a contract with the company that owns the pipes, saying that it will put enough gas into the pipes to meet the demands of its customers.

The gas providers know how many customers they have and how much gas they are likely to use from the customers' gas meters, so they pump in enough gas to meet these demands.

The customers, in effect, receive a mixture of the providers' gases – but as it is the same product, that makes no difference. At the end of each quarter, the amount of gas the provider has pumped in, and the amount of gas its customers have used, is worked out. If the provider has not pumped in sufficient gas, it is fined by the pipe owners.

How do sweet-makers get the letters to go all the way through seaside rock?

Rock is made from sugars. First the sugars are heated up to about 300°C to make a syrup, some of which is coloured. The rest is put through a pulling machine in which lots of tiny air bubbles are included, giving it a white colour.

The rock at this stage is still hot and as it cools down it becomes like Plasticene and can be easily moulded.

While still warm, the rock is rolled into long, thin tubes. The letters are then made by placing coloured tubes in among white ones to make a large (say, 5cm across) version of a stick of rock.

This large stick of rock is put on to a "batch roll", which keeps the rock in its cylindrical shape, and it is then extruded by hand, becoming thinner and thinner until it is the desired size and shape.

This process has to be done when the rock is still soft, so it has to be done quickly. The maximum number of letters that can be put in a rock depends upon the speed and expertise of the rock-maker. If the rock becomes completely cool, and therefore hard, before the above procedure is finished, the whole lot has to be thrown away.

Where is the temperature probe to measure the outside temperature located on a car, and why is it not affected by wind chill and/or engine temperature?

The probe is under the front bumper, protected from wind chill (which only really affects humans anyway), and far enough away that its readings are not affected by the engine's temperature.

How do rechargeable batteries work?

Normal batteries are actually distorted and largely destroyed in the process of making electricity.

In the recharging process, a current from an outside source is pushed through the cell in a direction opposite to that from which it was drawn originally. This reverses the reaction that happened during discharge, restoring the anode to its metallic state, reoxidizing the positive electrode.

Nickel-cadmium rechargeable cells comprise alternating layers of porous, negative cadmium anode and porous, positive nickel oxide cathode separated by absorbent layers, all permeated with electrolyte and all inside a nickel-plated steel case. Both the cadmium anode and the nickel oxide cathode material are contained in plates. The plates are conductive, increasing efficiency. Because of this design, the anode structure is not seriously distorted as the cadmium is oxidized, nor is the cathode structure as the nickel is reduced. This gets over the biggest problem of recharging batteries – the distortion.

What is the name of the super-absorbent material in nappies?

The material in nappies that absorbs urine is sodium polyachromade. It starts off in the nappy as a powder and can absorb 30 times its weight to become a gel.

Why do batteries that are running down recover slightly if you don't use them for a while?

In a copper-zinc battery, a copper plate and a zinc plate sit in a dilute sulphuric acid solution. When the battery is working, small bubbles of hydrogen gradually form around the copper plate and prevent the flow of charge. When the battery is disconnected, some of the hydrogen disperses slightly. When you use the battery again, there is less hydrogen to block the flow of electrons, so, for a short while, the battery will work again. Then the hydrogen builds up, and again the battery fails to work.

What is the device in an infrared burglar alarm detector called, and how does it work?

The device which does the detecting in a burglar alarm is called a pyroelectric sensor. It consists of a number of crystal elements (usually lithium and antalate) which are sensitive to infrared energy and convert it into a small electrical signal (usually about 200 micro-volts). This signal is used by the rest of the device to trigger the alarm itself.

What is the name of the material used in T-Shirts that change colour?

T-shirts that change colour are dyed using Lenco dyes. Ordinary T-shirts are certain colours because the dyes that they have been dyed with have electrons in certain positions within each atom. The position of these electrons determines the wavelength of light given off by the T-shirt. Lenco dyes are made of chemicals in which the electrons can be moved around, altering the wavelength and thus the colour of the reflected light.

Why don't aircraft spin their wheels before landing to stop the wheels from skidding?

When landing, an aircraft's wheels either have to spin at exactly the same speed as the aircraft or not be spinning at all otherwise the plane can skid. In order to get the wheels spinning at exactly the speed the aircraft is moving at would need a motor attached to each wheel. This would add too much weight and expense to make it worthwhile.

Why don't we have solid, slash-proof tyres for cars?

When tyres were first invented, they were solid. But the pneumatic tyres used today on cars make journeys smoother and more comfortable as the air inside them cushions the car from bumps. Until solid tyres can be made which will cushion the passengers as much as those filled with air, the idea of having slash- or puncture-free tyres will remain just an idea.

Why is glass transparent?

Normally, when light hits something it excites the electrons within its atoms and these then de-excite giving out light of a certain wavelength, which relates to the colour that we see. Atoms have levels and the electrons are excited between them. With transparent materials, these levels are so far apart that light does not possess enough energy to excite the electrons and so the light passes straight through without interacting with the material.

Why do racing cars have fat tyres?

Tyre size is controlled by "maximum shear force", which determines a car's turning capabilities. The equation for this is: maximum shear force equals normal force multiplied by coefficient of friction. Therefore, if the area of contact the tyre makes with the surface is great, the pressure is reduced, the coefficient of friction is increased, the maximum shear force increases – and the car can corner at high speeds.

Where does newspaper ink come from?

Newspaper ink is made from carbon black, which is finely-divided carbon produced by the incomplete burning of hydrocarbons, such as methane. The pigment particles are very fine and, because it is up to 95 per cent carbon, intensely black.

How is plastic made?

Plastic is made by a process called polymerisation. This is where chains of molecules (made up mostly of carbon and hydrogen atoms) are stuck together to make very long chains of molecules and networks. The raw material the chains of molecules come from is usually coal.

When a bulb blows, why does the fuse sometimes blow too?

When a filament in a light bulb blows, the bulb can arc (a spark jumps from one side to the other). The lamp then becomes a discharge lamp. The discharge has little resistance (since the bulb has very little gas in it) and this draws a lot of current, blowing the fuse. This effect can be prevented by putting nitrogen in the bulb.

How do you make chewing gum?

Chewing gum used to be made from thickened resin and latex from certain kinds of trees, or from various kinds of sweet grasses, leaves, grains and waxes. In ancient Greece mastic gum was chewed, and obtained from the mastic tree. Now the big chewing gum manufacturers make chewing gum synthetically from styrene-butadiene rubber, which is made from a reaction of styrene and butadiene.

What are the AHAs that cosmetics companies put in their moisturisers?

AHA stands for alpha hydroxy acid and is supposed to even out skin tone. However, it isn't one specific chemical. It is the general name for acids found in fruit or other foods. For example, glycolic acid (the acid in sour milk) and lactic acid (produced by tired muscles) are AHAs.

What does the term "smokeless zone" mean?

Smokeless zones were introduced in 1956 to try to solve the smog problem in Britain. So much fuel was being burnt that it was creating a smoky fog – a smog – that killed several thousand people during the winter months. Smokeless fuels do not produce particulates such as soot and ash, so they do not create a smog.

What is the purpose of the spirals that you see around tall chimneys in factories and hospitals?

These spirals were developed after World War II to "shed vortices". Any tall, thin structure will have problems remaining upright because of the wind. The spirals help to stop the chimneys being blown over.

What is dry ice?

Dry ice is frozen carbon dioxide which turns straight from a solid to a gas. If water were like dry ice, it would go straight from ice to steam without being a liquid in between.

How is concrete reinforced?

Reinforced concrete, which has been used since the middle of the 19th century, has metal bars or wires embedded in it for extra strength.

How can soft leather sharpen a razor?

As a blade is used, its edge is dulled – a "burr" is formed on either side that widens the blade. This makes it blunt. By dragging the blade across a leather strop the burr can be removed to give it a thin edge again. Strops aren't so effective on thicker blades such as scissors because the bulk strength of the material is greater. However, strops can be more effective on carbon steel knives and scissors because the carbon steel is weaker than stainless steel.

Why does static electricity affect water?

Everything is made up of atoms. Atoms themselves are made up of smaller particles such as a nucleus and "orbiting" electrons. An atom is a bit like a small solar system – just as the Earth goes round the Sun, so electrons go round atoms. Without electrons things would not dissolve, have a colour or conduct electricity. Static electricity is also caused by electrons. Atoms usually have an equal number of electrons (which are negative) and protons (which are in the nucleus of the atom and are positive). So the electrons balance out the protons. This means the atom has no "charge". By removing electrons from or adding electrons to atoms, they can be made negative or positive. When you rub a comb or plastic ruler, you are taking electrons away from the atoms in the comb. So the comb becomes positive – there are more protons than electrons. If you then put the comb near something negative, it will be attracted to it. Water is a special material in that it is made up of two different atoms called oxygen and hydrogen. When these two atoms join together, they share their electrons but they don't share them equally. The oxygen atom likes electrons more than the hydrogen atom, so

it takes more than its fair share of electrons. This means the oxygen is slightly more negative than the hydrogen. So the comb, that is slightly positive, will attract the slightly negative oxygen and pull the rest of the water with it.

Is it true that there are about a million germs on every pin-head?

Before we can answer this, we need to say what a germ is. Normally we say a germ is any living organism that we cannot see but that makes us ill. "Germ" is a general word which can describe a bacterium, a virus, or a fungus. It is true that there are probably a million bacteria on the head of a pin. Bacteria are all around us.

However, unless we stab the pin deep into an arm or a leg, these bacteria will not harm us.

If atoms are mainly space, why doesn't your hand fall through a table?

Everything around us is made of atoms – even the air we breathe. The difference between the air we breathe and a table is that the atoms are much more tightly packed in a table. So while you can pass your hand through the air – where you are essentially pushing atoms out of the way – you can't put your hand through a table because the atoms can't move out of the way. It's like trying to walk through a tennis court filled with 100,000 tennis balls as opposed to one with 100 tennis balls – you just can't do it.

But it's not just the space that's a problem. There are also very strong forces holding atoms together. So although atoms are mainly space, the forces holding them together and the tightness with which they are packed mean you can't put your hand through a table.

Why is it so difficult to iron out a crease when it's so easy to make a crease?

The Home Laundering Consultative Council says it's all to do with the direction in which the fabric fibres are lying. The fibres prefer to be in straight lines and when you iron in a crease you align them in that way. It is quite easy to get the fibres to do what you want because they want to do it too!

However, because this is their preferred position, it is not easy to iron out a crease once it's there. This involves making all the fibres jiggle up again. The best way to get rid of creases is to dampen the fabric so that the fibres relax and thus become easier to realign.

Why does a kettle go quiet just before it boils?

As water is heated, dissolved gasses in the water start to come out of solution. As water approaches boiling point all the dissolved gases have been released so there is no more bubbling. This is when the kettle goes quiet. As the water then begins to boil, the convection currents in the water become

very violent and the water becomes noisy again.

Why doesn't lightning affect people inside a car?

There's a special effect in a hollow sphere of metal, called a Faraday Sphere, where there isn't any electricity inside the sphere. Faraday, the man who came up with lots of the rules on electricity which we now use, first found out that a hollow sphere has no electricity in it.

Why do you get dizzy when standing on top of a tall building?

For the same reason that you can easily walk along the edge of a pavement, but not along the edge of a chasm. Your eye is not used to seeing objects at a great distance where the floor should be. The perspectives that the brain expects are not there, and it causes the body to over-correct for the apparent discrepancy. The resulting confusion in brain signals, and general anxiety caused by being in a potentially dangerous situation, cause dizziness.

How does the cut-off switch in a kettle work?

The switch is made of a strip of three pieces of metal sandwiched together, each of which expands at a different rate when heated. Steam from the kettle goes into the switch chamber at the back of the kettle and heats up the metal sandwich. The metals' varying expansion rate makes the strip buckle, pulling out of the circuit a metal bar attached to the switch. This breaks the power supply to the kettle element, and the kettle switches off.

Sometimes when you boil water in a microwave and then add coffee granules, you get a fizzing noise. Why?

For water to boil, or freeze, there must be nucleates in the water. These can be anything from small impurities to coffee granules that the water can boil off or freeze around. When you boil water in a pan, you get convection currents that disturb the water, letting in bubbles of air for the water to boil off, which also allows the water to boil away. This doesn't happen in a microwave so the water becomes superheated (reaches above 100°C without boiling). Once you add the coffee granules, the water suddenly releases all the energy it has stored up inside by boiling instantly and becoming steam. This is the fizzing noise you hear.

It can be quite dangerous if the water is heated excessively or is in a container that doesn't radiate the heat away very well. There have been stories of cups of water "exploding", sending coffee granules and boiling water over the person making the coffee.

You also get a fizzing noise when you add boiling water to black instant coffee – but not when you have sugar in the cup. Why?

If it is freeze-dried coffee, then air pockets get trapped in the coffee grains. Adding water dissolves the coffee and the air in the pockets is released to give a fizz. Sugar must act like anti-bumping granules, allowing bubbles to form more easily and continuously. Without sugar, bubbles are less easily formed, so the air pressure tends to build up until the bubbles burst off and fizz.

Why do ice cubes go white?

When ice is made in a freezer, the freezing starts from different points within the cube, ie, the crystal structure of the cube isn't uniform. When light enters it, you get refraction and reflection inside the cube so light doesn't go straight through and the cube isn't transparent.

Why does milk get a skin when it cools down?

The skin is a complex of casein, a milk protein, and calcium. It is the result of evaporation at the surface of the milk, which concentrates the proteins there. Skin formation can be minimised by covering the pan or by whipping up a little foam, both of which slow down the rate of evaporation.

Why are so many drugs addictive?

People can get addicted to all sorts of substances, including alcohol, nicotine, cannabis, opiates, cocaine, antidepressants and even chocolate. Scientists think that addictive substances stimulate a "pleasure pathway" in the brain. Making certain activities pleasurable – such as eating, drinking and sex – ensures that we continue these essential functions, which aids our personal and species survival. Addiction probably happens by the same system, but it is often harmful rather than helpful. Addictive drugs seem to affect the pleasure pathway so that the person needs more and more to get the same feeling. Stopping generally leads to distressing withdrawal symptoms, which tend to push the addict back towards use of the drug.

How do fruit or potato-driven clocks work?

In exactly the same way as a battery! Inside a battery there is a chemical concoction called an electrolyte. This contains lots of charged particles. We then need two conducting rods of different materials (in the case of a battery these are often carbon and zinc, in the case of the potato clock they are simply metal rods, perhaps

brass and steel). They must be of different materials because they must have different reactivities. The negative particles in the electrolyte become attracted to the more reactive one. In this way negative particles build up at one metal and positives at the other. If we join a wire between the two, the electrons in the wire move away from the negative particles and towards the positive ones. A current will flow in the wire, which, although it is quite small, is enough to run a small clock or a torch bulb.

Why, when you fan yourself, is the air cold even when the surrounding air is hot?

The fanning of air doesn't cool it down; it merely makes you feel cooler. The coolness is caused by various factors. The increased airflow over your body makes sweat evaporate from the skin, and this change in state (from liquid to vapour) draws energy (heat) from your body, thus cooling you down. Wind chill is also a factor: this is a measure of how cold you feel when you are exposed to a wind. For example, if the temperature is 5°C and the wind speed is 20°mph, the wind-chill factor takes you to minus 6°C, although water will not freeze.

Why is chicken-pox called chicken-pox?

There is some suggestion that chicken-pox's name arose because of the mildness of the disease, compared with smallpox; or that it has some distant connection, or possibly even origin, with chickens.

Another explanation is that this

name is an allusion to chick peas – from the Latin word *cicer* meaning chick-pea – due to a vague resemblance of the pox's skin eruptions to chick-peas.

How do the chemicals in hair dye change the colour of your hair?

Hair colour is down to melanin, which produces the various shades from blonde to black. Melanin is produced by cells called melanocytes that live within the hair follicles.

There are two main types of hair dye and they work in different ways. Dyes that contain peroxide – a bleach – strip out all the melanin and replace it with the dye. In this case if you stripped away the coloured dye you would be left with no colour at all. Semi-permanent dyes, such as those that last for six to eight weeks, work by just coating the shaft of the hair with colour. These types of dye can be removed to reveal your natural colour as they do not affect the melanin inside the hair.

We know that staying out in ultraviolet (UV) light can cause skin cancer – but is infra-red light hazardous, too?

UV light has a shorter wavelength than visible light, and infrared light a longer wavelength. In general, the shorter the wavelength, the more energy a photon imparts when it hits a molecule. UV photons (say, from the Sun) can carry enough energy so that if they hit a DNA molecule, they can change the chemical structure of a piece of the genetic code so it does not work properly. This can lead to mutation and cancer. Infrared light carries far less energy (less even than visible light) because it has a longer wavelength. This energy warms rather than damages, and is dissipated as heat. Thus infrared light should only damage us by overheating us, and you tend to notice when this is happening. Although UV is far more dangerous, it takes a while for the sunburn it causes to become apparent, so that we can cause ourselves quite a lot of damage without being aware of it.

Why do bad eggs float?

As soon as an egg is laid it starts to lose moisture through its shell. This moisture is replaced by air, which makes the air sac in the egg larger, and the egg less dense. At the same time, proteins in the egg white break up, producing hydrogen sulphide – which smells horrible. This gas eventually makes the egg light enough to float.

The animal kingdom

Do fish blink?

No. Like snakes, they don't have moveable eyelids. Instead, they have a transparent eye protector permanently in place. Fish have excellent eyesight and can see parts of the spectrum we can't. They rely heavily on visual signals for species recognition, choosing a mate and territorial defence.

When a cat gets fat, do its whiskers grow longer?

No. The length of a cat's whiskers are set genetically. If a cat grows fat, the whiskers become too short to be useful as "width guides". The cat could get stuck if it tries to squeeze through a hole that its whiskers tell it it can get through.

Why don't bats make a sound out loud ?

Bats do make sounds but our ears aren't sophisticated enough to hear them. Bats make sounds at a very high pitch, so high that it's called ultrasound. Like dolphins and whales, bats use sound to locate their prey and to work out where they are and where they want to go. It's called echolocation. The sounds the bats make bounce off objects like buildings, trees, animals and so on, similar to an echo. The bats listen to this echo and can then determine how far away and what shape an object is.

So bats can hear the sounds they make, but we can't.

Do giraffes have valves in their arteries to stop the blood in their necks flowing back to their hearts?

No – but then no animal does. Giraffes are mammals, as are humans. In terms of bodily structures and internal organs, everything is much the same (if different in shape). The circulatory system consists of a pump (the heart) which pushes blood into the arteries. These connect with the veins through capillaries. Arteries do not have valves, veins do: as the blood leaves the heart it is travelling at very high pressure, and doesn't need valves to ensure the flow is in one direction. Pressure in the veins is low. The movement of blood returning to the heart is helped by a series of valves preventing backflow.

How much better are dogs at smelling than humans?

It is thought that dogs are a million times better at smelling certain scents than humans. There are a number of reasons. A dog's nose has four times the volume of ours, and while a human nose has about 5 million ethmoidal (olfactory) cells, some dogs have over 200 million. A dog's nose is designed to pick up scents – it is large and wet, which collects and dissolves scent particles. When a dog finds a scent it starts salivating – the wet tongue also helps to pick up and dissolve more scent particles.

Why can't chickens fly?

Although chickens have lost most of their ability to fly, they still have the same characteristics of other flying birds and can fly short distances. They have air sacs around the lungs for efficient breathing and their bones contain numerous air cavities that make them lightweight for flying.

Domestication and selective breeding over the years is mainly responsible for them having lost the ability to fly. Archaeological evidence from human settlements in Indo-Pakistan dating back to

3250BC shows that chickens have been domesticated for thousands of years. They have been selected for their meat quality, the white meat on the breast and even possibly the fact that they are bad at flying. Centuries of unnatural selection have resulted in the present-day chicken, which is an incredibly poor flier.

How many teeth does a great white shark have?

The front teeth of sharks are constantly replaced by rows of teeth growing behind them. The adult great white shark has an average of 30- 34 teeth in its front row. Each tooth has a new one ready to swing into place, so the actual number of teeth in the shark's mouth is 60-68, of which only half are in use.

Why are there no mammals smaller than a shrew?

The answer to this question comes down to heat loss. Shrews are mammals, so in common with other mammals, they maintain a constant body temperature that's nearly always above that of their surroundings. As a result, they lose heat from their bodies to their surroundings. The source of the heat is the energy that the mammal gets from food. The more heat is lost, the more food is needed to replace this energy loss.

Heat loss is a bigger problem for smaller animals because they have a high surface-area-to-volume ratio: they have a lot of surface area to lose heat through. And, as the smallest mammals, shrews suffer from heat loss like no others. As a result, they need to eat a prodigious amount of food to stay alive.

This principle explains why mammals that live in cold climates tend to be large (for example, polar bears). These have quite a large volume for a relatively small amount of surface area, so they do not lose heat so readily.

Any mammal smaller than a shrew would not be viable on a heat-loss basis. If you think about animals smaller than shrews, they are always cold-blooded, for example, insects.

Do any animals have eyeballs that retract when they close their eyes?

As they lack well-developed eyelids, frogs do withdraw their eyes into their sockets while they are in resting mode. They are also able to use their eyeballs during swallowing, in order to help push food down their throat. They retract one eye at a time, which presumably creates some kind of peristaltic motion

Does a spider have a heart?

Spiders have hearts, but they aren't as complicated as ours. The spider heart is really just a tube that hangs at the back of the abdomen cavity. Two or three pairs of openings called ostia are found on either side of the heart. Through these blood enters, and is pumped forwards and backwards from the heart. Back flow is prevented by valves. This means that the heart keeps the blood pumping whatever position the spider is in – even if it

is upside down. The spider has an open circulation system: although blood travels through blood vessels to a specific area, it then flows into the open spaces and bathes the cells with oxygen and nutrients.

What makes the muscle of a bird "white" or "dark" meat?

White and dark poultry meat results from the amount of a pigment in the muscle called myoglobin. This pigment is closely related to haemoglobin, an oxygen - carrying component of blood. The oxygen-carrying ability of myoglobin allows the muscle to continue to work for long periods of time using a process called oxidative metabolism. Once all the oxygen "stored" in the muscle's myoglobin is used, the muscle then uses a process called anaerobic glycolysis to produce the contractions needed for work. If the muscle is used repeatedly for extended periods of time, the amount of myoglobin in the tissue increases. That is why migrating birds such as ducks and geese have darker meat in the breast muscles (the muscles used for flight). Chickens' legs are also muscled with darker meat because the birds tend to use them more than those in the breast.

Why shouldn't you give dogs human chocolate?

Chocolate contains theobromine, which is poisonous to dogs. A dose of 50mg per pound can be fatal to a dog. Milk chocolate contains 45mg of theobromine per ounce and unsweetened baking chocolate contains 400mg per ounce. Just one ounce of unsweetened baking chocolate can kill a small breed dog. Theobromine, when ingested by dogs releases epinephrine causing the heart to race and serious cardiac arrhythmias.

Signs include vomiting, diarrhoea, excessive urination, and hyperactivity followed by depression, coma, seizures, and death.

Why do birds all sing first thing in the morning?

Territories and defended areas are maintained during breeding season. The birdsong, an auditory signal, is used to attract mates, warn off rivals, alert other birds to danger, and, in the case of young birds, beg for food.

The best time to hear birdsong is at dawn. The dawn chorus is one of the marvels of nature. Birds all over the world show the greatest amount of singing activity around dawn, from English woodland to tropical rainforest. But why they do it at this particular time is still not clearly understood.

One reason may be that dawn is the best time for sound to travel, because there is little wind and less noise. Songs broadcast at dawn can be 20 times as effective as those broadcast at midday. And this is a time when birds can't do much else. Light intensity is low, making it difficult for them to hunt and forage. Low temperatures keep their insect prey on the ground.

By singing at dawn, when their energy reserves are low after the night, male birds may be telling

females that they are still fit for breeding. Dawn may be a good time to sing, but there is likely to be a lot of vocal competition.

So there are advantages to singing at a different time of day, particularly when two different species have similar songs.

Is it true that tortoises should not be fed on peas because it makes their shells go soft?

There is some truth in this, but it is not black and white. Basically, tortoises should not be fed too much of any of the pulses. Pulses are fattening, strange though this may seem, and this can disrupt the shell structure. In an adult, the shell wouldn't go from hard to soft; rather, there would be a build-up of the wrong sorts of fats around the liver and kidneys, rather like cholesterol. On the other hand, young tortoises are growing rapidly, and too much fat and protein in their diet would result in a soft shell. Tortoises should be fed as varied a diet of fruit and vegetables as possible, together with a full vitamin and mineral supplement. Also, if the tortoise is being kept indoors over the winter, they should have a daylight tube.

How do chickens sit on their eggs without actually breaking them?

The eggs survive the experience because hens are designed so that when they are incubating their eggs, they do not actually sit on them. Hens' skeletons are shaped so that the eggs can fit underneath the hen but none, or very little, of the weight of the hen is on the eggs. The feathers act as insulation to keep the eggs warm and it is the feathers that give the impression that the hen is sitting directly on top of the eggs.

Why doesn't the blood in bats run to their heads when they're hanging upside down?

Your circulatory system adapts to whatever position you are in – heart, arteries, capillaries and veins all work to move the blood through the circulatory system in one direction. Bat hearts are large, relative to body size, compared to other mammals. The position of the heart is also modified in many "microchiropteran" bats, so that it is in a nearly sideways position. Bats also have high stroke volumes (amount of blood pumped by the heart in one beat cycle), so they have large hearts and high heart rates. Valves in the heart prevent back flow, and there are modifications of some of the arteries, veins and capillaries that allow bats to regulate the amount of blood circulating through flight membranes. They can reduce or even stop the circulation to parts of the wings to control heat-loss across the membranes.

Do any animals eat bees?

Yes; bees have many enemies. The bee-eater is the most common enemy from the bird world. Badgers and skunks dig up bees' nests for the honey but they also eat the bees themselves. Field mice and shrews will attack bee nests. Wax moths lay their eggs in bee nests and the caterpillars ruin the bee egg cells by burrowing through them.

How fast can an alligator or crocodile run? Can a human outrun either one? Would it be safe to climb a tree or can they jump heights on dry land?

Crocodiles can go really fast if they gallop – but only a few species can do this. The fastest ever recorded was the Johnston's crocodile, which can reach speeds of up to 17kph (10.6mph). In general, crocodiles can reach 14kph, and this can be beaten by an average human, especially as crocodiles can only sprint short distances. Crocodiles rely on ambushing their prey and do not pursue it once it knows it is being chased.

It is sometimes said that the best way to escape crocodiles or alligators is to run in zigzags, exploiting their lack of peripheral vision. In fact, it is best to run in a straight line, as this is the shortest route to go the furthest. But don't climb a tree –

patience is one of these creatures' virtues, and they will sit underneath with an open mouth for a week, if necessary.

How can animals eat raw meat safely, yet we can't?

We can eat raw meat, and some dishes are considered a great delicacy. But we generally eat cooked food for two reasons. We prefer the taste of it, and cooking protects us from poisoning by contamination.

Animals usually eat meat fresh, or within a few days of the "kill". Cooking the meat will destroy almost all of the bacteria and viruses that can make us sick.

Animals, on the other hand, have built up a far better tolerance to such contamination. Domestic animals such as dogs and cats come somewhere inbetween ourselves and their wild relatives, and have slightly different ways of dealing with foods. Cats protect themselves by being very careful feeders; their phenomenal sense of smell will warn them if their food is at all "off" and they will not eat it. Cats also eat grasses to make themselves sick if they have to. Dogs are scavengers. Their digestive system is very tough and can cope with almost anything, but they, too, will vomit readily if they eat noxious things.

Cows eat green grass. So why is their milk white?

The colour of the food animals eat doesn't really determine the colour of what comes out – and this is especially true in a cow, where the grass is completely broken down as it passes through its four stomachs, by which time it no longer has a colour. So the question becomes, why is milk white? This is because it's an emulsion – one liquid completely suspended in another. Milk is a fine dispersion of calcium caseinate suspended in liquid.

How do poisonous spiders make poison, and why don't they poison themselves when they do?

Spiders have a pair of venom-producing glands behind their mouthparts. Poison, or venom, from each gland passes down a tube which takes it to the opening at the end of each of the pair of fangs where it is ejected only when the spider bites – and into its prey. Thus the spider never comes directly into contact with its own venom.

Why don't male mosquitoes bite?

The majority of mosquitoes don't bite. Of those species that do, only females require the additional blood as a protein source for the development of their eggs. Mosquitoes tend to get their energy from eating rotting fruit, not from drinking blood.

Is it a myth that there's a bird that eats bits out of alligators' teeth? If not, what is the bird?

Some birds have been said to pick food debris from the gums and teeth of crocodiles in Africa, usually those that are basking. However, this has never been officially observed. Some suggest that the Egyptian plover or the spur-winged plover may be responsible. Both species are known to associate with basking crocodiles, feeding close to them and on their ectoparasites (eg flies). Such behaviour is also seen by the common sandpiper, whilst in Africa during the northern winter. All three of these birds are waders.

How can a bite from a small insect paralyse humans?

From insects to snakes, many creatures paralyse their prey using toxins, which interfere with the working of muscles or nerves. When you want to move, your brain sends messages to the nerve fibres that activate muscle contraction. These release the neurotransmitter acetylcholine (ACh), which binds to receptor sites on the muscle surface. Many toxins are targeted at this region. For example, venom from the deadly black widow spider causes a massive release of ACh from the nerve fibres, whether or not the brain has told the nerve to fire. This exhausts the finite supply of ACh in the nerves and a victim can no longer move muscles. Some snakes use another method: the bungarotoxin in venom binds to the ACh receptor, blocking the chemical messages to the muscles. As a result, the victim is unable to move.

Why do dog faeces (if not cleared up) eventually turn white?

In the past there were two reasons. The first was diet. Dogs were fed home-prepared food with bits of bone in it, which put small chips of white material into the faeces.

However, bone can cause all sorts of problems for dogs – from chipped teeth to a scratched oesophagus. It can cause salmonella, and constipation. Modern dog owners prefer to use a prepared food with a milk-based calcium source, so dog faeces is no longer white because of bits of bone.

The other reason is that a mould starts to grow on the faeces if it's left for long enough. The mould – a yeast – takes three or four days to grow. But these days councils tend to clean the streets more quickly, removing the faeces before the mould turns it white.

How are mollusc shells made?

The shell is formed by the mantle, a thin sheet of tissue covering the body of the mollusc. Specific cells in the mantle produce a matrix that quickly becomes mineralised with calcium carbonate. This is what makes the shell hard. The rate at which the shell is formed and its thickness will be controlled by physiological (internal) and environmental (external) factors. The mantle will continue to secrete matrix until the mollusc and its shell are fully grown.

Some shells may take up to six years to reach adult size, although some continue to grow throughout the animal's life. The process of laying down the shell will vary depending on the nutrients available in the environment. This is why shells of the same species can differ although the shape of the shell will be genetically

scaring other animals away: it is the largest animal on Earth. An animal this large could not survive on land because its own weight would squash it. In the sea, it has water to support it against the effects of gravity.

If I crush an ant that is crawling in my kitchen, other ants clear its corpse away. Why? Do they subsequently eat it?

Most social insects have a well-documented behaviour called necrophoresis which involves the recognition and removal from the nest of dead nest-mates and other decomposing materials. Worker ants recognise the corpses by a number of chemical breakdown products: research by E.O. Wilson, the famous myremecologist (studier of ants), showed that if the "dead ant" chemical is sprayed on a live ant, workers will quickly carry it out of the nest, just as they would a corpse. The live ant then cleans itself off quickly and re-enters the nest – sometimes to be removed a second or third time if it hasn't cleaned itself properly.

Why don't whales get the bends?

The simple answer is that they are breath-hold divers, and do not breathe compressed gas at depth like scuba divers. Hence there is less nitrogen available for absorption and what there is was taken in at atmospheric pressure. However, it is more complicated than that. Human breath-hold divers can get the bends through repeated, relatively shallow (20-

metre) dives. Dolphins diving below about 70 metres are protected by alveolar collapse – the tiny sacs in the lungs purposely shrink – which prevents gaseous exchange taking place. But the mechanism by which whales avoid the bends on shallower diving schedules is not completely understood.

Why are crocodiles scaly?

One of the main functions of crocodile scales is protection. This function is further reinforced by some of the scales (particularly those of the back) containing a deposit of bone ("osteoderm"); the heavily ossified scales along the back of a crocodile are commonly therefore referred to as the "armour".

How long do slugs live?

The life expectancy of slugs varies greatly, depending on type, size and so on. But in general, very small slugs live about six months, while very large slugs can live for between eight and ten years.

Is it true that wombats produce square faeces? And which way do their pouches open?

Wombats do, indeed, produce cuboid faecal pellets. They are solitary creatures which live in burrows in Australia, and come out at night to feed mainly on grasses. They mark their territory with splashes of urine – and their strangely shaped faecal pellets. Their pouches, along with those of other marsupials that crawl along the ground, open in the opposite direction to that of a kangaroo: if the wombat was to stand on its back legs, the pouch would open downwards.

How many legs do centipedes and millipedes have?

Centipedes have one pair of legs per body segment and millipedes have two pairs per body segment. As the number of body segments varies, it is impossible to give a definite answer. But it's not 100 and 1,000.

Snakes continue to grow, although very slowly, throughout their lives. Did this also apply to dinosaurs?

Continual growth occurs in many reptiles, but is particularly noticeable in larger species of chelonians (turtles, tortoises) and crocodilians (crocodiles, alligators and gharials) as well as large lizards (such as monitor lizards). It is one reason why it is so difficult to be certain about the record sizes achieved by these creatures. Microscopic studies on bone from a wide range of dinosaurs indicate that it was probably universal among that group, too.

Why do moths fly towards light?

Because they think it's the moon. Moths are used to navigating by the light of the moon – they fly keeping the moon on one side. When a bright, artificial light is present, they try to do the same thing but to keep it in a fixed position they end up flying round in circles. The brightness of the light disorientates

them and their orbits get smaller and smaller until eventually they hit the light.

Why were there such large dinosaurs and mammals years ago?

Organisms tend to become larger as their lineages evolve; this is sometimes known as "Cope's rule". Many factors may interact to influence evolutionary trends in body size. For the largest dinosaurs, increase in size is likely to be correlated with exploiting a new food source: the sauropods literally grew taller with the trees on which they fed. And one way for a carnivore to tackle large prey is to grow large, too. It may sound simplistic, but there was nothing to prevent the sauropods (or mammals) from growing large – except, finally, sheer physical constraints.

The reverse is also true. As far as dwarfing is concerned, reduced habitat area is a driving force. Examples are island faunas of dinosaurs (Romania) or Tertiary mammals (Mediterranean islands) where the animals have become smaller as an adaptation to living in restricted areas. It is unlikely that giant lineages will evolve again – we humans have too much influence on habitat and ecology

Do any animals other than humans cry to show emotion?

Most scientists think humans are the only animals that cry to show emotion. While the eyes of certain animals (dogs, chimps, dolphins, etc), do water, this does not constitute crying. We don't really know why humans cry either; although it definitely elicits a sympathy response from most people; and there is a difference in the types of proteins present in the water of tears to those present when eyes water normally.

How strong is a crocodile's bite?

The muscles that close a crocodile's jaws are very strong. They crush turtle shells with ease, and a large salt-water crocodile holding a pig's head in its jaws can crush the skull from a "standing start". But the muscles involved in opening the jaws aren't so strong. A rubber band around the snout is enough to prevent a crocodile 2 metres long from opening its mouth.

What types of corpses are the scatopsid (filthy fly larva) found on?

Scatopsidae is a rather poorly known family of flies (Diptera), at least in terms of their biology. As far as it is known, most species breed in a variety of decaying plant and animal materials, eg rotting wood, damp compost, excrement and decomposing fungi. They are not typically associated with corpses, although some can breed in a wide variety of decaying substances and therefore could possibly do so in carrion at times, but as far as I know this has not yet been observed. Adult scatopsids are most often seen on flowers, and large numbers may sometimes be seen on vegetation following mass emergence near a breeding-site.

How does a fish know what species it is? It can't look in a mirror to see what it looks like and then find others that look similar. I guess this applies to all animals – how can a baby elephant recognise an adult elephant, without seeing itself in a mirror?

A deceptively simple question. Fish recognise their own species by, eg: luminous organs, in lantern fish; colour spots, in John Dory; smell, in chemicals released by an injured minnow.

We do not know whether, or how, they can recognise individuals of their own species. The recognition-response to these signals is usually genetic, ie they do not need to learn it from parents. They don't have to see themselves, only respond to a particular smell or colour that indicates another member of the species. It seems that fish, and presumably other animals, know what patterns and colours to look for by some genetic coding – it's just natural! However, it's clear that some animals don't recognise, or feel comfortable with, others of their own species if they're older and bigger. I foster an elephant that was recently introduced to a new family in Kenya. It had no memory of adult elephants, as its mother was killed when it was young. It took a couple of hours to feel comfortable with the adult elephants.

How do you determine the sex of a tarantula?

When tarantulas are young they all look like females, but as they get older their sex becomes more obvious. Adult males have hooks on their front legs and their stomachs are smaller than females'. Also, the males' "pedipalps" (the feely bits that stick out of the head) are shaped like clubs. However, it may take 10 moults, or about seven years, for these differences to become obvious.

What is the smallest spider in the world?

The smallest spider is the Mygalomorph spider from Borneo, whose body measures just 0.5mm long – the size of a coffee granule. The largest is the goliath bird-eating spider, the largest of which has a leg span of 29cm (11in) – the length of your forearm.

How long do spiders live?

Ordinary spiders live for about a year, although up to five to six months of this may be spent in the egg stage. However, some South American tarantulas can live for as long as 20 years, while some tropical jumping spiders only live for three months.

Do bears hibernate?

Hibernation, a state of torpor, dormancy or inactivity, is used by some bears and other animals to adapt to a shortage of nutrition during the winter. Bear hibernation differs from that of other animals.

Not all bears hibernate. Bears that live where the winter does not get too cold do not hibernate. Similarly, bears that have not put on sufficient fat stores may not hibernate, or do so only for a short time. During the hibernation of bears, they do not eat, drink or defecate. Their urea is reabsorbed through the bladder wall and safely converted into usable amino acids and protein. Their metabolism slows down. Their body temperature drops, but never below 89 degrees. They require only half their normal oxygen intake. Their digestive organs and kidneys shut down almost completely. There is no permanent loss of muscle functioning or bone mass. They exist solely on fat and fluids in their body. They do not dehydrate. They lose up to 40 per cent of their weight, from fatty tissues. They use approximately 4,000 calories per day to maintain their body. Blood circulates more to the brain and upper body. Some bears hibernate for seven or eight months.

How is snake venom produced?

Venom is produced at the back of the snake's head (behind the eyes). Glands similar to those that produce our saliva make and store a cocktail of venoms, toxins and enzymes, which travel through ducts to either fangs or groves in the teeth. The venoms work in different ways: they can paralyse prey (cobra venom affects the nervous system) or digest tissues and organs (rattle snakes) which helps them in their food intake.

How strong is an ant?

Ants can carry up to 50 times their own body weight on their backs, and their pincers can grip something 1,400 times their weight.

By contrast, even the strongest humans can lift only a few times their own weight.

What is the smallest bird?

The bee hummingbird, Mellisuga helenau, of Cuba and the Isle of Pines, measures about 2.5 inches long (57mm), half of which is taken up by the bill and tail, and weighs 0.05 ounces (1.6 grams). The females are slightly larger.

How do cats purr?

Recent research suggests that in domestic cats it is the vibration of an elastic ligament linking the clavicle bone to the throat – which creates a purr during both inhaling and exhaling. In their larger cousins, things are slightly different, restricting the purring to an out-breath only. Neither kind of cat ever stops purring – they just control the volume – with loud purrs conveying anything from anger in a Snow Leopard to contentment in a Tabby!

What are male and female emus called?

The male emu is the "rooster", the female is the "hen". Just-hatched babies are "chicks", 10-to-15-month-olds are "yearlings", and 16-to-23-month-olds are "coming twos".

Is it true that there is a one-eyed fish called a Cyclops?

No, but there is a small crustacean with one eye called a Cyclops. They are small (rarely more than half an inch long), can be green, orange, blue or red, have a red or black eye, and swim in salt or fresh water depending on the species.

This group of crustaceans is called the copepods, so Cyclops are a type of copepod.

What is the life cycle of the crab louse?

The female crab carries eggs under her abdomen, which resemble bunches of grapes, and are a bright orange colour when first laid. This colour then gets darker, and sometimes the eye-spots of the larvae can be seen through the egg case. The larvae hatch as zoea, which look like tiny commas and can swim. After a number of moults, the zoea develop into a megalop stage, which has legs and claws, but its tail is still visible. A small appendage on the tail can help the megalop to swim. The megalop moults and changes into a small crab and the tail, instead of protruding, is now tucked under the body of the crab.

Do other mammals – especially primates – have monozygotic identical twins?

Yes, basically. For example, the nine-ringed armadillo, roe deer and coypu all have monozygotic twins.

How high does a grasshopper jump?

The largest known grasshopper in the world is an unidentified species from the border of Malaysia and Thailand, measuring 25.4cm in length. It is capable of leaping 4.6m.

To jump as high as possible, the grasshopper makes its body streamlined. The wings remain closed, and the legs straighten and tuck under the body. Although small, the grasshopper's leg muscles are hundreds of times more powerful than an equal weight of human muscle.

Is it true that armadillos are the only mammals apart from human beings that can produce twins?

No, there are many mammals that produce twins. Armadillos are unusual because they are the only mammals to produce identical monozygotic quadruplets (four genetically identical offspring).

What is the average lifespan of a horse?

According to the Science and Technology Desk Reference book, the maximum lifespan of a horse is 62 years. Obviously not all horses will live this long and an average value will be somewhat less than 62 years. The lifespan of a horse will depend on, amongst other things, the conditions in which it lives and the pressures that are put on it during its life.

Do animals get addicted to substances?

Yes. It seems animals, like humans, can get addicted to substances that are of no biological value. Rats, trained to inject themselves with cocaine, continue to do so even after they start having extreme reactions like seizures.

We cannot assume that rats become addicted for the same reasons as humans, or by the same mechanisms, although similarities in brain structure suggest common "addictive" pathways.

A good example of a useful addiction in nature is the koala bear's love of eucalyptus leaves. Koalas will die without them. This addiction is acquired, rather than chosen, as the koala cub gets used to the eucalyptus in its mother's milk. But there are also benefits. Eucalyptus leaves contain precious water. They also contain aromatic oils which help to keep the bears' fur free of parasites, relax their muscles and lower their blood pressure. Other animals eat plants, fruits and berries (for example, opium poppies and rotting fruits) which contain intoxicating substances.

How many species of shark are there?

There are approximately 350 different species.

Why is it that dogs see only in black and white?

In fact, they don't; they have colour vision, but it is similar to that of red/green colour-blind people. In human beings, the retina at the back of the eye has three types of "cone" (colour-sensing cells) – blue, green and yellow (often known as "red"). Dogs have only the blue and yellow ones, which means in practice that they are unable to detect the difference between red and green, although they can distinguish between yellow and blue. It is thought that only animals such as birds and primates, which need colour vision in order to distinguish between ripe and unripe fruit, need colour vision.

However, dogs are highly sensitive to changes in movement because their eyes have a greater than usual number of "rods" – important for black-and-white vision – which contributes to their hunting ability.

How deep can a sperm whale dive?

They are known to dive to 350m (1,150 feet) but the deepest was found tangled in cables 1,134m (3,720 feet) down.

Do fish hear?

Yes! Carp, particularly goldfish, are considered to be hearing experts. They have three bones, the Weberian ossicles, connected to the swim bladder and vibrations are transported to the brain. Some fish also sing. In California some people living in houseboats heard a buzzing at certain times of the year. Rumour put it down to aliens but it was eventually found to be the noise a Micharen male fish makes to attract the females.

How much dung does an elephant produce?

About 150kg of dung a day – about 24 stone, or one tonne of dung a week.

Mysteries of the Cosmos

Is it quiet in space?

Yes. Sound can't travel in space so all those science fiction movies where there's sounds of rockets blasting away are completely wrong. If you and I were standing in space (if we could do that without space-suits) and I shouted at you, you wouldn't be able to hear me.

How big is our galaxy?

Our galaxy is about 50 kilo parsecs. A parsec is 3.26 light years and a light year is the distance light travels in one year. So that makes the galaxy about 1,500 million billion kilometres across.

Why doesn't a spaceship burn up when taking off, just as it does on re-entry?

When the spacecraft takes off it is not moving fast enough to rub hard against the dense atmosphere. This means it does not heat up too much. By the time the spacecraft is going fast enough for heating to occur, the atmosphere it is travelling through is not dense enough to rub against the spacecraft's sides, so, again, heating doesn't really happen.

On re-entry, on the other hand, a spacecraft is moving much faster than it is on take-off, so it rubs against the atmosphere much more. It is also gathering speed as the atmosphere grows denser.

Can you shine a laser on to the Moon?

Yes, lasers can be shone onto the Moon, and the NASA astronauts that landed there took mirrors with them. These mirrors are used to measure the distance to the Moon very accurately, by reflecting the laser light back to the Earth. If the time taken for the light from the laser to go to the Moon and back is carefully measured and the speed at which the light is travelling known, then the distance can be calculated.

What are stars made of?

They are made of very hot gas, mostly hydrogen and helium. The gas gets denser and hotter as you head towards the centre of the star.

Is the Earth's spin slowing?

Yes the Earth is slowing down, but only slightly. In fact, the amount it is slowing down by is so unnoticeable that we don't need to worry about it. But we can tell it's slowing over millions of years. In Jurassic times (65 million years ago) the day was only 16 to 18 hours long. Since then the spin has slowed so the day is 24 hours long.

What is a blue moon?

There are two definitions of a blue moon. The first is a phenomenon caused by ash and dust which is ejected by volcanic eruptions into the upper atmosphere. When light reflected from the Moon passes through the atmosphere, it interacts with the volcanic materials, resulting in a blue casting as seen from the ground. A second definition of a blue moon is when two full moons occur in the same month; this happens once every 2.72 years. The next blue moon is on 31 December 2009.

Is the Earth getting closer to or further from the Sun?

The Earth is neither moving away from nor moving closer to the Sun. For the Earth's orbit to change, there would need to be some gravitational force making it change – like a large nearby planet. Nothing like this exists so the Earth's orbit stays the same.

Where does the Solar System end?

It is quite difficult to give a precise answer as to where the Solar System ends, but there is a definition for its end point. The edge of the Solar System is the point where the influence of the Sun stops.

As you read this there are space probes heading out of the Solar System, looking for its very edge. The Sun is emitting a solar wind, which blasts out of the inner solar system. The edge region is called the heliopause; this is where the solar wind hits interstellar gas and stops, creating a standing shock wave around the Solar System. No one is entirely sure just how far away the heliopause is.

Why do satellites move so rapidly across the sky?

To keep in orbit they have to move fast. The velocity at which satellites have to travel depends only on the height above the Earth and the Earth's mass. If a satellite travels slower than it needs to, it will spiral into Earth. If it moves faster it will break away and head into space.

The International Space Station, for example, orbits at a height of about 400km and takes only 92 minutes to orbit the Earth once. This is pretty fast; the station generally takes only a few minutes to cross the sky. However, some satellites are sent into a geostationary orbit; they still travel very fast but they follow the Earth's rotation, so from the ground it appears that they are not moving at all.

Why do planets spin?

The planets spin and rotate about the Sun. The Sun itself is spinning and revolving around the centre of the Galaxy. The entire solar system was formed from a massive ball of gas and dust. Shock waves from nearby supernovae created ripples in the ball that forced bits of dust and rock to clump together. This in turn encouraged further bits to stick together, and so on. So why did this whole mass start spinning?

Essentially, this is down to a law called "the conservation of angular momentum". This says that as something gets smaller, it spins faster. So, as a skater brings their arms in to their body and

gets smaller, they speed up. Any slight rotation in the ball of dust and gas would have been amplified as it shrunk to form a planet. This initial rotation could have formed during one of the supernova explosions, or in a collision with another ball of gas.

Would it be possible to escape from a black hole?

It depends how close to the black hole you got and how big the black hole was. Only if you came closer than a distance called the "event horizon" would you definitely not be going home. But this distance varies in size, depending on how much mass the black hole consists of. Black holes really are very dense: to make the Earth, which has a mass of 6 million billion billion kilograms, into a black hole, it would have to be squashed into a sphere that would fit into the palm of your hand. You would have to get pretty close to a black hole like that before you even noticed it.

Why don't stars appear in pictures from the Apollo landings on the Moon?

The lunar surface is very bright, and reflects a lot of light. The television cameras on the Moon compensated for this by reducing the amount of light let through the lens. As a result, stars were not bright enough to be seen.

How far does the Earth travel round the Sun?

About 570 million miles (900 million kilometres). The first

measurement was made by Aristarchus of Samos in about 270BC. He measured the position of the Sun relative to the Moon when the Moon was half full. From this, he worked out the distance to the Sun (since the Earth's orbit is nearly circular, the distance travelled is 2 *pi* multiplied by the radius). The number he got was 20 times too small, but very early astronomers often did worse.

Stars twinkle because of the Earth's atmosphere. Why don't planets?

Stars are so distant that they appear as point sources of light, so any disturbance in the Earth's atmosphere is easily visible. Planets, being closer, appear more as a disc than a point of light. Any disturbance is less visible because if the central part of the image is distorted as it passes through the atmosphere, that distortion probably won't reach the edge of the disc – so the planet won't seem to twinkle.

What is the Big Crunch theory in astronomy?

Physicists hold that if the universe contains enough matter, then its present expansion – the result of the original "singularity", or Big Bang – will one day be halted by the gravity of all its matter, and then begin to contract. This will culminate in a "Big Crunch" in which all matter is crushed out of existence. The key unanswered question is: does the universe contain enough matter to cause this, or will it just continue expanding forever?

How does the technique of using planets to speed up satellites work? Doesn't this slow the planets down?

The planet's gravity is used as a "slingshot" to speed up the satellite on its journey. In the process, the planet does suffer a slight loss of its momentum. But the amount is negligible. For the Voyager flybys of Jupiter, for example, the planet's lost energy resulted in Jupiter's orbit being slowed down by about one foot per trillion years.

What are wormholes, and do they really exist?

In modern physics and cosmology, wormholes are at present just a theory rather than a proven phenomenon. The theory describes them as short cuts in space, associated with black holes. Imagine you leave your house and go for a walk from Wembley to Aberdeen. At Wembley is a black hole into which you disappear. You then immediately appear out of a wormhole in Aberdeen and continue your journey to the local pub. The distance actually travelled in our space is simply the distance from your house to the black hole plus the distance from the wormhole to the pub. The bit of the journey between Wembley and Aberdeen is never actually travelled. Because you're not actually going very far, it doesn't take very long. To an outside observer though, you have travelled from Wembley to Aberdeen, and very quickly. That observer, calculating the speed of the journey, would suggest that you had travelled faster than the speed of light. In reality your speed was no faster than your normal walking speed; you just shortened your journey. So wormholes don't actually speed you up, they just make your journey shorter.

What are white dwarf stars?

White dwarfs are small, dim stars which are reaching the end of their life. They start as normal stars, and then go through a period of intense activity near the end of their life, during which they expand and become hundreds of times larger than usual – a "red giant". Then they run out of stellar fuel, and cannot sustain their overblown size. The star then collapses, forming a super-dense white dwarf star. However, stars which are more than 40 per cent bigger than our sun do not collapse, but explode as a supernova. Our Sun will end its days as a white dwarf – in about five billion years.

What is antimatter?

Antimatter is matter that is in all respects the opposite to "ordinary" matter except mass. The charges of antimatter particles are the opposite of ordinary matter – so the equivalent of our negatively charged electron is positively charged (called the positron). An antihydrogen atom (one of which has been made on Earth) consists of a positron and an antiproton.

Matter and antimatter interact through the same forces as matter, but when they meet, the result is total annihilation.

Where do comets come from?

Comets are made up of rock and ice left over from the time when the solar system was formed. Dutch astronomer Jan Oort suggested in 1950 the existence of a cloud of comets 50,000 times as far away from the Sun as is the Earth. The Oort Cloud is thought to contain about 100 billion comets, some of which can get nudged out by gravitational interactions with passing stars and then fall into closer, elliptical orbits about the Sun. Other comets may also come from the Kuiper Belt, which is closer to the Earth than the Oort Cloud but contains smaller objects.

What shape is the Universe?

The Universe is what is known as a hypersphere. A hypersphere is almost impossible to visualise, as it is a four-dimensional sphere – it alters with time. However, you can use the analogy of an onion to describe it quite well. Imagine the universe as it is now, this very instant, to be the outside layer of an onion. If you could look out into the universe as it is now, you would be looking around this shell. If you could look far enough, you would look right round it and see the back of your head.

But we cannot look at the universe at this very instant, because as we look out we are looking back in time. You can imagine that everything you are looking at that is at the same distance – say, five light years away – is on the same shell of the onion. The further away you look, the closer you are looking to the centre of the onion. These layers do not exist in this state any more (in terms of place or appearance) as they have moved (with the expansion of the Universe) since the light left them, but this is how we see them. You cannot travel from one side of the outer sphere (the universe as it is now) to the other side through the centre, as the centre is not just empty space; there is no space. You can travel only around the shell itself, as this is where the space exists. Well, we said it was hard to visualise.

What are shooting stars?

Shooting stars are meteors – small bits of rock and dust floating round the solar system that glow brightly as they burn up in the Earth's atmosphere. Sometimes they are mistaken for UFOs.

How did Uranus's satellites get their strange names?

In 1787 William Herschel thought he had discovered several Uranian satellites (though only two were later confirmed). In accordance with the custom of the time, he only gave them numbers. In 1851 William Lassell discovered two more. Because of the confusion over Herschel's unconfirmed satellites, Lassell consulted Herschel's son John and decided to give the confirmed satellites proper names. John Herschel wrote: "Proceeding from without, inward in succession, the names Oberon, Titania, Umbriel and Ariel, of the fairies, sylphs and gnomes of Shakespeare and Pope have been assigned respectively." The subsequent Uranian satellite discoveries (Miranda by Gerald Kuiper in 1948 and the 10 satellites discovered by the Voyager 2 spacecraft in 1986) have been named from the same sources.

How much rubbish is there floating in space?

The bits of old satellites and rockets that orbit the Earth are a serious problem. There are about 7,000 major objects orbiting the Earth and only about 100 of them are still working. There are also 40,000 smaller bits and pieces, mainly debris of exploded rockets. Then there are over three million particles, such as flakes of paint, specks of insulation and exhaust fumes. The Mir space station and the Space Shuttle have been hit by flakes of paint which have – at a speed of 18,000mph plus – pitted the windows. Collisions with "space junk" are now a hazard for satellites, rockets and astronauts alike.

How many meteors collide with the Earth in a typical year?

We don't know exactly, but many tonnes of material hit the Earth every year. The solar system is strewn with material left over from comets and asteroid collisions throughout history. As our planet sweeps through space, it goes through this debris which creates the streaks of light in the atmosphere that are meteorites.

In the past, larger bits of rock have collided with the Earth creating impact craters, and destroying vast tracts of the Earth's surface. But these large pieces of rock have mostly been swept up already, so these large impacts don't happen very often – fortunately.

If all the matter in the universe was concentrated into such a small space just after the Big Bang, why didn't gravity just pull it all back together again?

Because of inertia. The primeval stuff was flying apart so fast after the inflationary push that gravity could not pull it back instantaneously. If the universe were "closed" then eventually, after all that outward momentum had been used up, gravity would triumph and the universe would close up again – as predicted by the Big Crunch theory (see page 90). But recent measurements suggest the universe contains only 20 per cent of the matter required to pull it together again, which implies that it will continue expanding forever.

Why are rockets launched vertically, not horizontally?

In the past, the simplest way of getting into space was by using a staged, vertically-launched rocket. It had to be staged because we didn't have materials lightweight enough or engines powerful enough to build a single-stage-to-orbit (SSTO) rocket. Vertically-launched SSTO rockets are now theoretically possible with powerful new engines and super-

lightweight, durable, materials for the propellant tanks and structure. But 90 per cent of the take-off weight of such a SSTO rocket is propellants.

AeroSpacePlanes are also theoretically possible. They take off and land horizontally, use wings to get the benefit of lift from the air they are flying through and can be "just" 70 per cent propellants at take-off. Their drawback is that they work by using atmospheric oxygen, which is sucked in through air intakes while in the lower atmosphere to burn the onboard fuel. They only switch to onboard oxygen when the air gets too thin. The engines are very complicated: projects like the British HOTOL and NASA X-30 (NASP) have always floundered owing to expensive development.

Of Jupiter's moons, why is Europa made of ice and not Io?

The Sun and other planets formed from a huge cloud of dust, ice and gas billions of years ago. Close to the (hot) Sun that was forming, temperatures were so high that only rocks could exist. Further out, ices could exist as well.

The best current theory for planet formation claims that dust/ice grains collided and grew in size to eventually form "planetesimals" (little planets). At some locations in the solar system there was a local "clump" of these planetesimals – the points at which planets grew. As other planetesimals were attracted to these locations by gravity the planets grew in size to form the bodies we see today. So, planets near the Sun are rich in rocks and metals – especially Mercury. The planets further out are "gas giants" with icy interiors. Their moons are mainly icy with some rock mixed in; less so further out in the solar system.

If you look at Jupiter and its moons as a mini-solar system forming out of this huge cloud of gas, ice and dust, then near the hot Jupiter only rocks could exist. So Io, being closer, is mainly made of rock; as you get further from Jupiter there are a lot more ices mixed in with the rock – like on Europa.

Is it just a coincidence that the Moon takes the same amount of time to rotate as it does to go round the Earth?

The two rotational rates are not a coincidence. The Moon is locked in what's known as a "synchronous rotation". The Earth raises body tides on the Moon (basically, it stretches it) which are about 20 times greater than body tides on the Earth. The enormous energy dissipation that results has slowed the rotation of the Moon to result in an equilibrium, whereby the Moon's rotation (27 days) is the same as the time it takes to revolve around the Earth. Thus it always presents the same face to us.

As a consequence of tidal forces, the Moon is actually moving away from the Earth. The angular momentum of the Earth-Moon system must remain constant; the Earth's momentum is decreasing, owing to tides raised on its surface; and, in order to conserve momentum, the Moon increases its angular momentum by moving away.

Some of the satellites of the outer planets (Jupiter, Saturn, Uranus and Neptune) have also become trapped in synchronous orbits.

Where are the 'Voyager 1' and 'Voyage 2' spacecraft now?

Voyager 1, launched in September 1977, is moving at 3.5 astronomical units (AU) per year along a trajectory angled 35° north of the ecliptic. (One AU is the distance between the Earth and the Sun, about 93 million miles.) It is moving towards the Solar Apex – the direction of the Sun's motion relative to nearby stars. It is currently more than 9.615 billion km from the Sun, with signals taking 17 hours and 51 minutes to make it back to Earth.

Voyager 2 (it in fact preceded *Voyager 1*) is moving at 3.1 AU/yr along a trajectory angled 48 south of the ecliptic. It is more than about 7.628 billion km from the Sun – signals take 13 hr 41 min to reach us.

Both should have enough power to send data back to us until about 2020 – by which time they should have passed the heliopause, the point where the Sun's solar wind dominates and the interstellar wind prevails. They will pass within a few light years of nearby stars over coming millennia, but not close enough to be gravitationally attracted into orbit around them. The *Voyagers* have nuclear batteries, so they will be dead when their power levels run low; there are no solar panels on the craft to reactivate them if they pass near another star.

Was there ever running water on Mars? And is there any now?

Based on orbital photography, we believe that Mars once had an atmosphere thick enough to sustain liquid water on its surface. We have photographed valleys on Mars that appear to have been cut by running water; the Mars Pathfinder spacecraft touched down in one. In fact, billions of years ago Mars may even have had oceans. Today, its atmospheric pressure is only $1/100$ that of Earth's – so any liquid water on the surface instantly turns to vapour. The atmosphere must have been lost over millions of years. Exactly how is not clear, though Mars's low gravity means that it can't hold on to a thick atmosphere anyway. However, there is believed to be a layer of permafrost – permanent ice – just a few metres below the surface of Mars at mid-latitudes.

Sometimes you can see a halo of light around the Moon. What causes this?

There are two possible explan-ations. It could be a corona – a round patch of brightness, two or three times the diameter of the Moon, often with a hint of colour around its edge. This is caused by diffraction of moonlight by tiny drops of water in a thin veil of misty cloud, usually at low levels in our atmosphere. A corona often precedes a warm front, when the thin veil of cloud thickens and produces drizzle, and then possibly heavy rain.

Alternatively, there is an effect that is, in fact, known as a "halo". This is a much larger, bright circle around the Moon (radius 22 degrees) which is only bright at its outer edge. The halo is caused by reflection of moonlight from ice-crystals in a thin veil of high-level, cirrus-type cloud. A halo is often seen in spells of fine weather.

What is a red dwarf?

A dwarf star is a small, low luminosity star at the end of its life. Dwarfs are usually white, but come in a variety of colours that change as time passes and the star cools. Red dwarfs have a temperature of about $2{,}500°K$.

While stars are burning hydrogen, they are held together by gravity, and kept "inflated" by the heat and light these nuclear reactions generate. But once a star runs out of fuel it often becomes a red giant – a swollen expanse of gas at low temperatures. What happens next depends on the star's mass. Low-mass stars tend to lose their outer envelope of gas, which drifts off into space, leaving a small core – a white dwarf.

Matter in white dwarfs is a degenerate gas, a strange state where all the electrons are stripped from their parent atoms. Such gas is an almost perfect conductor of heat, and does not obey the ordinary gas laws. White dwarfs can compress to very high densities because there's little outward radiation from nuclear reactions; typically they are 10 tonnes per cubic centimetre. Such a white dwarf has no source of energy, and simply cools forever, becoming a yellow dwarf, then red, brown and eventually a black dwarf. This might take trillions of years, but the end state of a star like this is typically a ball about the same size as the Earth, but 50,000 times more dense than water, covered maybe with a thin layer of ice and surrounded by an atmosphere a few metres thick.

The Sun will become a white dwarf, but first will become a red giant engulfing Mercury and Venus, and blowing away the Earth's atmosphere and boiling the oceans. But that won't happen for about 5 billion years.

The Moon orbits the Earth every month. Why then isn't there a solar eclipse (where the Moon blocks out the Sun) every month?

The Moon's orbit is tilted in relation to that of the Earth around the Sun by 5.2 degrees. The lunar orbit does not oscillate, so the moon's orbital plane does not rotate as the Earth rotates around the Sun. This means that an eclipse only occurs if the alignment of Moon, Sun and Earth is exactly right.

Where do the Moon's and Earth's gravitational fields exactly balance?

About 62,000km (39,000 miles) from the Moon – which itself is 384,000 km (240,000 miles) from Earth on average – the pull from Earth and the pull from the Moon cancel each other out. The Moon's gravity is about one-sixth that of Earth's, and this distance is about one-sixth of the way between them.

This point is called the L1 (Lagrange-1) point between Earth and Moon. *Apollo 8* had a radio call from mission control when they passed this point in December 1968, on their way to the first human orbit of the Moon.

Is it possible to say how fast our galaxy is moving through the Universe?

Yes, by measuring the apparent Doppler shift of the microwave background radiation – leftover "noise" from the Big Bang. Since that radiation is not moving, and we are, we can measure the motion of the Milky Way rather accurately. The current best number is that we are moving at about 600 km per second in a direction away from the constellation Cygnus.

An interesting, unsolved question is, if we are moving, what is pulling us? Astronomers say it is the "Great Attractor" – believed to be just a local imbalance in the galaxy distribution, with a relatively local cluster of galaxies invisible behind the (southern) Milky Way creating a local gravitational attraction.

Is it possible that a planet could orbit the double star system Sirius A and B?

Sirius A is a type A1 star, with 27 times the Sun's luminosity, while Sirius B is a white dwarf with only 0.02 times the Sun's luminosity. You can consider Sirius B as being in a very elliptical orbit around Sirius A (actually, they both orbit their common centre of mass) with the distance between them varying from about 7 to 28 AU – where 1 AU is defined as the distance between the Earth and the Sun. As it happens, Jupiter lies about 7 AU away from the Sun, and Neptune about 28 AU away.

Current theories suggest that planets are very unlikely to form in a close binary star system: the companion star (in this case Sirius B) would tend to throw the "building blocks" for the planets out of the entire system, disrupting their formation. Theory also suggests that only stars whose mass is less than 1.5 times that of the Sun will have orbiting planets; Sirius A's mass is 2.3 times greater than the Sun's.

Why do the tails of comets look curved?

Comets in fact have two tails – ions, formed from charged particles forced off the "dirty snowball" of the surface, and dust, released as the ice melts on the approach to the Sun. The ion tail is straight, and usually points away from the Sun. It is the dust tail that is curved.

The particles that comprise it vary in size and velocity of ejection. The smaller ones, about a micron in size, experience the additional effects of radiation pressure, a repulsive force that can change the particle's orbit around the Sun. Rather than being part of the

main body of the comet, they are falling independently with their own momentum. The effect is that dust particles making up the tail are moving in different orbits, all similar to the comet's, but subtly different enough to give the characteristic curve.

How long and at what height and speed does the space shuttle orbit?

The type of orbit depends on the shuttle's mission. The Hubble repair mission was conducted at a record shuttle altitude of about 359 miles because that was where Hubble was positioned. The STS 70 mission which carried the Russian cosmonaut Sergei Krikalev, reached about 220 miles. The lower the orbit, the higher the orbital speed.

The speed of 160-mile high circular orbital speed would be about 17,750mph. There is not much difference between orbital speeds from 160 to 350 miles. One orbit takes about 90 minutes.

How many stars are there in a constellation?

The number varies a lot. They are counted by measuring the number of stars that can be seen in an area of the sky. The Southern Cross has lots of stars – 19.6 per 100 square degrees of sky. Most others have between five and six per 100 degrees.

An easier way is to count the number of bright stars. In the northern hemisphere, Centaurus has 18 bright stars. Canis Minor has only two.

Why does the atmosphere on any particular planet not "leak" into space?

For two main reasons: gravity and energy (at the molecular level). Some molecules do leak into space, while others don't have enough energy, as they are too heavy.

Atmospheres may be replenished by biological activity and also by the substances that are released from volcanoes.

How big is our galaxy?

Our galaxy is about 50 kilo parsecs (kpc) across. A parsec is 3.26 light years and a light year is the distance light travels in one year. So that makes the galaxy 1,500,000,000,000,000,000 kilometres across.

If the furthest reaches of the Universe are expanding at close to the speed of light then their masses will increase. Could this increase in mass, and associated increase in size, explain why the Universe is expanding?

It is true (according to Einstein's theory of Special Relativity) that objects moving close to the speed of light appear to increase in mass, but they will also appear to shrink in size. This is called the Lorentz contraction. The expansion of the Universe is, therefore, not due to Special Relativity.

How many people have walked on the Moon?

Between 1969 and 1972, a total of 12 American astronauts walked on the Moon, before the Apollo programme was cancelled prematurely by the US space agency Nasa. The 12 travelled in six separate Apollo missions and collectively spent approximately 80 hours outside the lunar lander, during which time they collected rock samples, took photographs and set up experiments.

What's the difference between an asteroid and a comet?

They can be difficult to distinguish. Essentially an asteroid is an irregular, rocky body that is smaller and less massive than a planet. About a million are thought to exist in the asteroid belt between Mars and Jupiter, and many more are scattered through the Solar System.

By contrast, comets trace elliptical, but regular, orbits that may take them far beyond Pluto and then close to the Sun. They have icy material on their surfaces or within, and emit gases when heated by the Sun.

Is anyone allowed to name a star?

Officially no. Except for the few dozen bright stars named by the ancients, stars are always designated by some alphanumeric system involving their placement in the sky, such as their ordering by position in a zone of declination, by brightness (or by variability of brightness) in a constellation, or simply by the digits of their co-ordinates in some system: in some instances the stars are simply given numbers in a catalogue by some astronomer or observatory who collected them for some specific purpose – such as their relatively rapid motions with respect to other stars or because of particular features in their spectra. There are organisations that will try to sell you a star, but they have no official right to do so.

Why do the Sun and Moon appear bigger when they are near the horizon?

This is a famous optical illusion that has no simple answer. If you take a ruler and measure the size of the Sun – or, more easily, the Moon – at the horizon, and then again when it's higher, you'll see that there is no difference. There has been much research into this topic. Many think that because we can see buildings and trees that we know to be not that far away, our brain tries to imagine the Sun or Moon at that distance too, and this makes them appear bigger. However, experiments in which people were asked to judge the size of the Moon with and without reference objects such as buildings suggest this is not the case.

Why don't the constellations change, if the stars are moving so fast?

Although the stars are indeed moving very fast (at a speed of many kilometres per second) they are so far away (typically trillions of kilometres) that they have to travel for thousands of years before we can see a difference in their positions. In one lifetime we won't notice a difference in the constellations, but if you could come back in 50,000 years' time, the sky would look very different.

What if?

Is it possible to build a chess computer that knows every move so that it wins every time?

Computers have "solved" some simpler games so that they always either win or, at worst, draw. Chess is a much bigger problem. Clearly, at every step of a chess game, there is only a finite (but large) number of possible moves: 20 at the start, and so on. The number of possible sequences of moves to the end of a game is also finite – though of course even larger.

So in theory one could "build a chess computer that knows all possible moves". In practice, however, the number of possible sequences of moves is astronomically large (400 just for the first two moves, after which it gets really hard), while the ultimate speed of computers is limited (for example by the speed of light and therefore communication within the computer).

So the shortest possible time needed just to compute all possible moves could be equivalent to many people's lifetimes. And this does not even consider the time needed to evaluate those moves and to determine the "optimum".

So the practical answer is no.

If you were standing on a pair of scales in an express elevator, and it was travelling at a steady speed up or down, would the indicated weight be different from the indicated weight when the elevator was not moving?

If you were travelling at a steady speed, the weight shown on the scales should be exactly the same as if you were stationary on the ground. You would not be acted on by any other force but gravity when you were travelling at a steady speed – so the force down (your weight) would be unaffected. When the elevator accelerated or slowed, then your weight would appear different because you would be experiencing a force. When you are going down – decelerating, you weigh more; accelerating, you weigh less.

When you are going up – decelerating, you weigh less; accelerating, you weigh more.

When a budgie in a cage starts flying, what happens to the total weight of cage and bird?

The total weight, as measured by a weighing scale under the cage, would go down. When the budgie is on its perch, the total weight is a combination of the weight of the cage and the weight of the bird. When the bird launches itself into space, its weight no longer has any effect on the scale the cage is on. However, if the bird were to be in an airtight container (don't try this at home), the weight would remain the same. This is because as the budgie beats its wings in flight, each stroke pushes down a column of air with the same weight as the bird.

How fast would a coin dropped from the top of the Eiffel Tower be travelling by the time it reached the bottom? Could it hurt someone if it hit them?

A falling object doesn't accelerate indefinitely. It speeds up until it reaches its "terminal velocity", after which it will continue to fall at the same speed. A coin dropped from the Eiffel Tower has a terminal velocity of about 45 m/s (about 100mph) – which would certainly cause some considerable damage to anyone unlucky enough to be hit by it.

How many slices of bread could you toast in a lightning strike?

One lightning strike is a billion kW – the power of about 800 million toasters; it could toast 1.6 billion pieces of bread. Of course, lining up all those bits of bread and turning them over after five milliseconds could be tricky.

How long would it take something to fall to the bottom of the deepest underwater ocean trench?

The Marianas trench is 35,839 feet, or 10,860 metres deep, and it would take about an hour for an object thrown overboard to fall right to the bottom.

In the film "Goldfinger", one of the women was painted in a non-porous paint which killed her. Would this really happen?

Yes, for several reasons. First, the skin is important for temperature regulation. We sweat constantly: it evaporates and removes heat from our bodies. Blood flowing near to the skin also loses heat as it is cooled by contact with the air. Without these two mechanisms, the body would overheat and we would die.

Secondly, the skin can absorb substances applied to it – such as any toxins in a non-porous paint. These might be eliminated by the

kidneys, or they might kill you.
Thirdly, a non-porous paint would
mean that the skin's waterproof
surface layer would get
waterlogged (like wearing a
non-absorbent plaster for a while)
and so be liable to infection. It
might even start to fall apart.

What is the speed of a bullet in a plane travelling at 1,000mph if the bullet leaves the barrel at 500mph?

If the bullet is fired forward then
the speed to somebody standing on
the Earth would be 1,500mph and if
fired towards the tail, 500mph.
To everybody on the plane it would
appear that the bullet was
travelling at 500mph no matter
which direction it was fired.

What position would you need to adopt in order to survive in a lift that was falling uncontrollably?

The thing that determines whether
you will survive such a fall is the
height the lift is falling from. If you
fall a great number of floors, it
doesn't make much of a difference
if you are in a lift or not. Being in a
free-falling lift is similar to jumping
off a building of the same height
and landing on something solid –
the forces on your body on impact
will be the same. In addition,
adopting a particular position may
well prove impossible.

If the lift is in free fall – so that
there are no frictional forces
slowing it down – then you would
be "weightless" inside it, like an
astronaut in space. Because you
and the lift are falling at the same

rate (all bodies, irrespective of their
mass, fall at the same rate under
gravity alone), you would not – in
theory, at least – have any physical
sense that you were falling at all.
Instead, you would be floating
around, quite unable to adopt any
position, because you wouldn't
even know which way was up and
which was down.

In practice, of course, you
probably would know, because the
roof of a lift is different from the
floor. You would also probably
hear and feel the air rushing past.
And the lift would probably not be
in true free fall, because it would
be banging around in the shaft,
but it would still be hard to
position yourself, as you would be
almost weightless.

Whatever position you managed
to get into, one thing is certain: you
would land with a considerable and
probably uncomfortable bang.

Light slows down when it enters glass. Is it theoretically possible to see into the past when you look through glass with a very high refractive index?

Surprisingly, yes – but not very far.
Put a piece of glass with an
amazingly high refractive index
over one eye, and nothing over the
other. The light passing through
the glass will be slowed down, and
arrive at the eye later than the light
from the same object that hasn't
gone through the glass. So one eye
would be seeing in "real" time,
while the other would see the same
view with a tiny delay on it.
However, the delay would be
fractions of a microsecond - it's not
much of a time machine.

Can you use a yo-yo in zero gravity?

Not properly. Gravity-reliant tricks such as "walking the dog" would be tricky, and "cat's cradle" would be impossible, but you could make the yo-yo leave and return to your hand by flicking your wrist. What would be bizarre would be the fact that the yo-yo could go up and down the string in any direction. It would move quite slowly, and whether it would spin is debatable. If it didn't, getting it to roll back up again would be tricky due to lack of tension in the string.

Which will hit the ground first, a bullet fired from a gun (horizontally) or one that is simply dropped from the same height?

Both bullets will hit the ground at the same time. This is because the horizontal and vertical motions of objects can be treated separately. So although the first bullet has to travel further across the ground, both bullets fall the same distance and so reach the ground at the same time.

If you were walking to the Sun, how long would it take?

The distance to the Sun is 93.5 million miles (149.6 million km). If you walk at about 4 miles every hour (which is fairly brisk) it would take you 23.4 million hours, which is 975,000 days or 2,671 years to reach the Sun. If a new generation occurs every 20 years and you allowed five years before a person started to walk, then it would take 107 generations to reach the Sun.

Plants and trees

How many seeds does a raspberry have?

A raspberry flower has numerous carpels arranged in a spiral, and every carpel has two ovules in it. The fruit is a compound structure and every drupelet (the succulent, lumpy bit) in it has a single seed. The actual number of seeds will depend both on the size of the whole compound fruit and on the size of the individual drupelets/fruitlets that comprise it. So a large fruit with many small drupelets will have many more seeds that a small fruit with a few large drupelets. On a reasonably vigorous plant with medium-sized fruits there will be about 50 seeds/drupelets.

How does the grass stay green?

Grass is a plant that contains different cells, many of which contain chloroplasts – the part of the plant which uses light to make sugar (which the plant then uses

for food). Inside these chloroplasts is a substance called chlorophyll which allows the chloroplast to use light. Light is made up of different colours, which is why you see sunlight as white (all of these colours mixed together). The chloroplast uses all the components of the light except the green part, which is why you see grass as green.

How much carbon dioxide is taken in by a tree in an hour?

This depends on the leaf surface area and the level of photosynthesis occurring (which regulates the concentration gradient between the outside and inside of the leaf). In turn the rate of photosynthesis is dependent on the species, nutrient levels and incident light levels. For a 100-year-old beech, for example, the rate is about 2.3kg per hour.

How do seed banks store seeds?

Seeds of the "orthodox" kinds are

dried down to about 15 per cent moisture content, and then stored in deep-freeze at -200°C. (The temperature of liquid nitrogen is -196°C.) The moisture has to be removed so the water doesn't damage the cell walls as it freezes, because it expands. Some kinds of seeds can be dried further and then stored in it, but structural changes – for example in seed coats – may occur.

Why do bananas change from green to yellow when they ripen?

During the ripening process, fruit produces ethene, a gas which permeates the cells of the edible parts. That makes the fibres in the fruit break down so the fruit goes soft. It also converts the starch to sugar, making the fruit sweet, and destroys the chemical that makes the fruit green – chlorophyll – so that other colours can come out. In the banana's case, that colour is yellow. By controlling the gene that switches on ethene production, scientists can dictate how fast, or even if, fruits ripen.

How do fungi differ from plants?

Fungi are quite like plants: they form complex, sometimes branching structures, they cannot move independently and they cannot respond to their environment as animals can.

The main difference lies in the way these two sorts of organism get their food. Plants can photosynthesise, using the light energy of the Sun to fix carbon dioxide from the atmosphere to form sugars. Fungi can't photosynthesise – they do not produce any chlorophyll.

Instead, they secrete powerful enzymes to break down the material of living or dead organisms. This becomes their food, which they absorb through their cell walls rather than ingesting it as animals do.

Fungi therefore have to grow in or on their potential food. Since they surround themselves with food-digesting enzymes, it is hardly surprising to find that their cell walls include a very tough protective material, chitin. (This material is also found in animal exoskeletons.)

Are apple pips poisonous? If so, how dangerous are they?

Apple pips actually contain cyanide, and you can be poisoned by them if you eat too many – though it would take about a cupful. You might be sick of apples by then.

Where does the red colour in some plants come from?

The red colour results from the presence of pigments known as anthocyanins. Anthocyanin production results from gene mutation, and is widespread in plants. It has been selected for (for ornamental purposes) in trees such as copper beeches and maples. Their leaves have the red colour in addition to the green of chlorophyll. They therefore photosynthesise normally.

Why do some wild flowers flower at night?

Flowers control various pollinating mechanisms – including attracting insects and other animals to carry pollen from one flower to another. Those opening at dusk tend to have moths and/or bats pollinating them; it would be a waste of energy to open at other times when pollinators weren't available. The flowers are usually very pale, and show up in available light at dusk. Sweet scent is a common feature.

How much oxygen do plants produce?

A mature beech tree produces enough oxygen for 10 people every year, and a lawn 35 metres square (300 square feet) can produce enough oxygen in a week for one person's daily demand. The Science Museum in Singapore had a fascinating exhibit to show the importance of green plants in producing oxygen and taking up carbon dioxide. It comprised a large fish tank with aquatic plants and fish in the water. Sealed inside the tank, totally enclosed by water, and linked to an oxygen trapping system, was a cage with healthy, vigorous hamsters in it. Food was provided through a sealed tube system, and the only oxygen they received was directly from the water plants in the surrounding tank.

What uses does the Aspilia plant have?

The genus Aspilia, a member of the Compositae (Daisy) family, is certainly interesting: it has representatives from tropical America through to Africa and Madagascar. The total number of species recognised in the last revision was around 60. It finds uses in solving many medical problems including eclampsia, lumbago, sciatica, neuralgia and malaria. It also has antibacterial and antiparasitic properties. This is not to say that every species will have one or more of these uses, or that the usage is proven as effective, but it is certainly a good indication of the potential bioactivity of members of the genus.

One fascinating aspect about members of this genus is the way that primates, particularly chimpanzees, also appear to use them for their medicinal activity; indeed it would seem that man has learned such uses from them.

Why do vegetables go soft when you cook them?

All plants are made up of millions of plant cells. Each plant cell is surrounded by a very strong cell wall and adjacent cells are held together by a glue. When you eat a raw vegetable or an unripe piece of fruit, your teeth need to break the glued cells apart and this is what gives you that "crunchy" feeling. Ripening or cooking softens the glue between the cells so that your teeth just slide between the cells.

What are lichens?

A lichen is an association between a fungus and an alga (sometimes a blue green "alga" which is strictly a blue-green bacterium). Lichens are slow-growing and highly resistant to drying out. Gravestone surveys show that some lichens grow as little as a few millimetres in a century. The alga photosynthesises and produces sugar or alcohols which the lichen can use as a food source. In turn, the lichen surrounds and protects the alga. Most lichens have evolved special (asexual) reproductive structures which ensure that fungus and alga are dispersed together. Each partner can also reproduce sexually.

Does talking to plants help them grow better? Many people think so, but is there any scientific truth behind it?

It would seem that there may be. Plants grow better when they have more carbon dioxide. The level of carbon dioxide in ordinary air is quite low, but the air we breathe out has a lot more. If you talk to a plant, you breathe on it, giving it extra carbon dioxide. However, to have any real effect, you would probably have to talk to the plant for several hours each day.

What is the tallest tree in the world?

The giant sequoia can reach more than 90m (270ft) in height and is the tallest living thing.

How do you tell how old a tree is?

Once a tree has been cut down, the number of annual growth rings seen on the base of the trunk can be used as a measure of the age of the tree. During spring and summer the rate of growth of the tree's cells is at a peak, and the xylem tissue laid down is made from relatively large, well-spaced cells. In the winter, cell growth is virtually nil – any cell division which occurs results in a narrow dark band of smaller, denser cells. Thus there will be one of these dark growth rings for each growth season.

Marram grass is killed by trampling, but Rest Harrow and Red Fescue grasses are not. Why?

Marram grass is a pioneer species that has adapted to colonising dunes under strenuous conditions. It has shallow roots and a stiff structure that is easily broken.

The other two are secondary species that are more adapted to long-term survival than colonisation, and are therefore not affected by trampling.

We are sometimes warned not to sleep in a room with plants in it. Does this mean that it is unhealthy to sleep in a forest?

The first advice may be right. During the day plants photosynthesise, releasing oxygen as a by-product. They also respire – using oxygen and releasing carbon dioxide – so some of the oxygen produced by photosynthesis in the daytime is diverted to respiration.
At night, though, plants only respire, taking in oxygen and releasing carbon dioxide. Therefore flowers and other plants should be removed from hospital wards at night, as sick people should not have to compete for oxygen with plants.

In a forest at night, plant respiration may marginally lower the available oxygen level. To most people, though, the difference would not be noticeable, and so poses no health risk.

If a pineapple is a fruit, where are its seeds?

The pineapples eaten today are different from wild pineapples still found in some countries. A pineapple is a compound fruit – it is made up of several sections all stuck together to make one bigger fruit. Each section has its own seeds buried beneath the skin in sacks. If you peel a cultivated pineapple, you can sometimes see the vaguest hint of the seeds that a cultivated pineapple's "ancestors" would have had. In the past, someone must have found a pineapple without seeds that was

managing to reproduce itself. This pineapple would have been produced accidentally by nature but, because there are no seeds, each pineapple has more fruit and is therefore more valuable to us. Farmers figured out that they could earn more by growing these types and so grew nothing else, so pineapples with seeds are now very rare.

Origins

Why is a scientist called a scientist?

The word comes from the Latin scire, which means "to know". A scientist is thus one who knows or learns. Before the word was first used, a couple of hundred years ago, scientists used to be called natural philosophers. "Philosophy" comes from the Greek words for "lover of true knowledge".

How were ancient buildings constructed so well without the benefit of modern building techniques?

Many ancient buildings had religious significance – which often meant they merited the best materials and methods of construction then available. Despite this, many did not not survive well: the Victorians did a great deal of restoration work on many ancient buildings and would often build completely new structures, as they did with

Canterbury Cathedral. A church founded in the 12th century is quite likely today not to have any original stones left in it. Westminster Abbey was built in 1065 – but none of the original materials remain.

How did Pascal measure atmospheric pressure with a 40ft glass tube full of wine?

Barometers can be made using any liquid. Imagine a long tube almost filled with water. Turn the tube upside down and put the open end in a bucket of water. The weight of the atmosphere on the water in the bucket pushes against the water in the tube and stops it coming out. The lower the atmospheric pressure, the more water will flow out of the tube, causing the level of water in it to drop. Conversely, high pressure will force the level up. Barometers are usually made of mercury because it is so dense – 76cm of mercury in a thin tube can typically be supported by an average atmospheric pressure. Pascal showed that the same atmospheric pressure, which most people were unaware of until then, could support 40ft of wine in a tube.

Why are modern British copper coins (1p and 2p pieces) magnetic, whereas old ones are not?

In 1992, the metal used to make coppers was changed from bronze to copper-plated steel. This makes them magnetic.

Who invented ball bearings?

The idea of using balls as anti-friction devices was first suggested by Leonardo da Vinci in the 16th century, but, as with many of da Vinci's ideas, it wasn't put to use for a long time. In 1794, Philip Vaughn from Carmarthen got the first patent on a bearing which resembled modern ball bearings; but it wasn't until steel became economically available in the late 19th century that steel ball-bearings, like those we use now, became popular.

Why was 24 hours (1/15 of 360 degrees; four "minutes" equivalent to one degree of longitude) chosen to divide up the day, when 36 hours (1/10 of 360 degrees; 6 "minutes" equivalent to 1 degree longitude) would seem more logical?

Historical questions are always difficult to answer definitively. But most Western civilisations – Greeks, Sumerians, Babylonians, Egyptians, Romans and western Christendom - assigned 24 hours to a day, 12 of daylight and 12 of darkness. (It didn't matter that the length of an hour varied according to the seasons.) It might have been more convenient in retrospect if time had matched the units of rotation, but they came from different sources. The figure 24 came from 2 times 12, and was derived in Babylonia from the Sumerian sexagesimal method of reckoning (based on gradations of 60 – 5 times 12 – not multiples of 10, because they had a base system of 6). Babylonians then subdivided each section of the day into 30 gesh. This was then doubled to give 60 minutes some time later - but we don't know exactly why.

Where did the peculiar name of the fundamental particle called a "quark" come from?

In 1964 Murray Gell-Mann and George Zeweig thought up the theory that introduced these particles to explain how protons and neutrons and other similar particles behaved. Gell-Mann had just been reading *Finnegans Wake*, by James Joyce, which contains the phrase "three quarks for Muster Mark". He decided it would be amusing to name his particles after this phrase.

How big is the Great Pyramid in Egypt?

The Pyramid of Cheops, also known as the Great Pyramid, is 147 metres high, with sides 230.4 metres long.

What were the first words spoken on a telephone?

They were: "Come here Watson, I want you," and they were spoken

through an ionisation chamber creating ions and generating a current. As smoke entered the chamber, the number of radioactive particles decreased so the current decreased. This set off the alarm.

by Alexander Graham Bell, inventor of the telephone, on 6 March 1876.

Who discovered the electron?

Sir Joseph John Thomson, an English physicist (1856-1940), found the new particle in April 1897. Without his discovery, it is doubtful whether we would be using electricity today.

When were fire alarms invented?

In 1852, DL Price filed the first patent for a fire alarm. It had a bi-metallic strip (two pieces of metal that expand at different rates when heated) that bent as the temperature rose until it made a connection in a circuit containing a bell. In the 1880s, a system was developed using a network of mercury thermometers around a house. As the temperature rose, the mercury rose until it made contact with two platinum electrodes which completed the circuit and set off the alarm. Smoke detectors weren't invented until the 20th century. In 1941, W Jaeger and E Meili from Switzerland developed a system very similar to that used today. They had a radioactive source whose radiation passed

How did the Romans do multiplication? Instead of 103 times 22 would they have had to manipulate CIII x XXII?

The answer is, with great difficulty. Instead of calculating with pencil and paper, they would have used an abacus to actually do the calculations, and then written the answer in Roman numerals. Division would have been even harder – involving breaking the calculation into a number of operations like those we now use in long division.

You might wonder why they didn't develop a positional number system like ours: the answer is probably because they didn't have a symbol for "zero" (try doing maths without it) which was introduced later, by the Arabs.

Where does the word "photon" come from?

The term comes from the Greek word phos or photos, meaning light. But the word photon wasn't used until 1926. Before that a "particle" of light was called a light quantum.

Who kept the first weather records?

Our Eurocentric view of science and technology sometimes fails to credit the debt we owe early scientists and inventors in the East. The study of oracle bones from the Shang dynasty capital of Anyang shows that systematic meteorological records were being kept as long ago as the 13th century BC. The Anyang oracle bones also refer to rainbows, which were thought to be visible rain dragons. In the Song period, in 1070 AD, a double rainbow was described as being due to the reflection of sunlight from suspended water droplets. This was two centuries before Qutb al-Din al-Shirazi, a Persian, first satisfactorily explained that, in a rainbow, light is refracted twice and reflected once through a water drop. In Europe, the use of such a simple instrument as the rain gauge only started in AD 1639, but there were rain gauges in Korea two centuries earlier and in China in the 13th century.

Where were dinosaurs discovered?

Dinosaurs were first found in the Western world in Britain in 1817, when quarrymen in the village of Stonesfield, in north Oxfordshire, discovered some megalosaurus bones. It was eight years before another dinosaur was found, in 1825, by Dr Gideon Mantell who called the animal iguanodon. Those bones were unearthed near Cuckfield in Sussex.

Where does the word "atom" come from, and who first thought of it?

The word atom comes from the Greek for "not cut". The first person to think that atoms existed – that is, that everything was made up of combinations of some indivisible objects – was a man called Democritus who lived in Greece in 400 BC. He thought that atoms were the smallest things that could exist, and this was generally believed until the early part of this century.

Who invented the seismograph?

This has been attributed to De la Hautefeuille (1703); the first modern forms were developed in 1848. Some books attribute the first modern pendulum seismograph to the German Emil Wiechert, in 1928. However, the forerunner can be traced to 132 AD during China's Han Dynasty. It was important then (as now) for the government to be forewarned of earthquakes.

Chang Heng, the Astronomer Royal, designed a fine-cast bronze vessel, 6ft across, with a domed lid and eight dragons' heads with bronze balls in their mouths, and eight bronze toads below looking up with their mouths open. A central column moved when an earthquake occurred, and pushed a slider; this dislodged the ball in a dragon's mouth, to fall into a toad's mouth, giving a rough indication of the direction of the disturbance.

There was a mechanism so only one ball could fall, as a protection against being set off by secondary tremors. Unfortunately none of these incredible objects has survived.

During the World War II in North Africa, I came across several large man-made caverns underground. What were they?

They were water reservoirs. Surface water is lost very quickly to the heat in North Africa so, many centuries ago, people built reservoirs underground in order to store water. Some still exist and can be found all over the desert.

Where did (urban) Victorians get their ice?

They had ships bring it down from icebergs, glaciers, and so on, and then they brought large blocks of it to their homes. They kept it in cool rooms in their houses and chipped off bits as necessary. Needless to say, this was very wasteful and made the ice very expensive, so only the rich could afford it.

Who invented the can-opener, and when?

There are three different dates involved. The first is 1858 when Ezra Warner of Waterbury, Connecticut, invented the can-opener – nearly 20 years after US canners switched from jars to metal cans and almost 50 years after the metal can was invented (1810). Previously, metal cans were opened with general-purpose tools – such as a hammer and chisel! In 1870 William Lyman of W Meridan (also in Connecticut) patented a can-opener that used a wheel for continuous operation, improving on the lever-and-chisel variety. A drawback was that the can had to

be pierced in the centre of the lid and the can-opener adjusted to fit each size of can. In 1925 a wheel-type can-opener was patented (we don't know by whom), which rode around the rim of the can on a serrated wheel and was similar to the common type of can-opener that we know today. This was also a predecessor of the electric can-opener as regards its mode of operation. So tin cans were around for a good 50 years before anyone came up with can-openers.

Did England once have different time zones within it, as the United States now does?

Not officially. However, before modern communications systems, when there was no way of telling people around the country what the exact time was, people relied on their local sunrise and sunset to set their clocks. As the sun rises and sets at different times across the country, this meant a difference in times between towns.

The arrival of trains, and timetables, enforced unification around a common time.

Who invented the rubber band?

According to Harwin Chronology on Inventions, Innovations and Discoveries by Kevin Desmond (1987), it was Stephen Perry of Messrs Perry and Co, Rubber Co Manufacturers, London, from vulcanised rubber.

Who first suggested that the Earth was spinning?

Nicholas Copernicus, in 1542.

Who was the first person to wear a watch?

The first known recorded wrist watch was made by two Swiss men, Jaquet-Droz and Leschot, in Geneva in 1790. It was a "watch to be fixed to a bracelet". The earliest surviving example is from 1806.

Who invented the fountain pen?

When pens were first invented, the nib had to be frequently dipped into a container of ink. This slowed down the process of writing considerably. As a result several people had the idea of creating a pen where the reserve of ink was attached to the pen. The first working version of such a pen was patented by LE Waterman in 1884, in the United States.

Why is Madame Curie so famous? What did she do?

Marie Curie is often portrayed as a sort of scientific saint – the Florence Nightingale of physics. In reality, like Florence, she was as tough as old boots and an able administrator. She was a left-wing atheist who at one point was involved in a terrific scandal: she was accused of breaking up another physicist's marriage, which eventually led to a duel. (Not involving her, though.)
Marya Sklodowska, as she was originally called, was the daughter of a Polish science-teacher. She went to study physics and chemistry in Paris, where she married a physics professor, Pierre Curie. In 1897 Marie decided to study radioactivity for her

doctorate. She began by working through all the elements then known, and found that uranium and thorium were radioactive. She then tried minerals and discovered that uranium ore (pitchblende) was far more radioactive than it should be for the uranium that it contained.

Marie suggested that the ore contained an unknown, but highly radioactive, element in such a small concentration as to be invisible. Having little money, she and Pierre were forced to work in an old shed that had been a mortuary. It took them four years to extract a tiny quantity of radium from several tonnes of ore. They took very few precautions against the radiation, and even today Marie Curie's notebooks are still too radioactive to handle.

She received two Nobel prizes for her work on radioactivity before she died of leukaemia at the age of 67.

Continuing the family tradition, one of the couple's daughters, Irene, and her husband discovered how to make things radioactive using neutrons. They also received a Nobel prize.

Who invented the light bulb?

In 1845, J Starr, an inventor in the United States, suggested using a filament of carbon as an electricity conductor enclosed in a glass bulb to produce light. In 1878, Joseph Swan, from Britain, developed a vacuum pump to remove air from the bulb so that the filament would not oxidise and burn away, but it wasn't until 1879 that Thomas Edison (of America) patented the world's first electric light bulb. Edison's bulb burned for 13.5 hours before it went out. However, Joseph Swan, from Sunderland, was the first to demonstrate an electric light bulb in December 1878 – shortly before Edison. He just didn't get round to patenting it.

What is the latest theory on Stonehenge?

Theories are constantly evolving, and the site remains an enigma. The general consensus these days seems to be that it was built as a monument to create regional unity, in a time when the area was in crisis after the land had been exhausted by cultivation. However, fresh excavation taking place in 2008 under the auspices of English Heritage may shed new light on the matter. It is thought that the complex may have taken 1,500 years to build and was used as a communal "place" or temple. London's South Bank complex, built to bind the nation together after World War II, had a similar function.

Who invented dinosaur names?

The word dinosaur means "terrible lizard". Individual dinosaur species were named by the scientists who first found them, often in Greek or Latin. They named them after some unusual feature about the animal, where it came from, or even who discovered it. For example, Baryonyx walkeri means Walker's heavy claw, because of the discoverer, Bill Walker. Velociraptor means "speedy hunter" and Tyrannosaurus rex means "king of the reptiles".

Where does the word "magnet" come from?

Ancient Greeks first found magnetic rocks in an area called Magnesia, in what is now Turkey – hence "magnet".

Who performed the first heart transplant?

Christiaan Barnard, a South African, performed the first heart transplant in 1967. His patient lived for only 18 days, but thanks to his work, many heart transplants are performed all over the world every year.

Why did penny farthings have such big wheels?

The larger the wheel in this early design of bike, the faster the rider could go, as the pedals were directly connected to the wheel without any gearing mechanism. The only way to make the bicycle travel further for each turn of the pedal was to enlarge the wheel to which the pedals were connected. This did make for some difficult bikes to ride, though, and the design was soon replaced by smaller models with gearing mechanisms.

Did Teflon exist before the space programme?

It is sometimes said that Teflon, which is used to make frying pans non-stick, contains Moon rock. This is, of course, untrue. In fact, Teflon was developed by mistake in 1938 by Du Pont's Jackson Laboratory in New Jersey, USA.

It was developed further for use in the space programme as a lubricant.

Oil cannot be used in space to lubricate moving parts because it boils away in the direct heat of the Sun. Instead, Teflon is used to coat the surfaces of any moving parts that might otherwise stick together.

Who invented the miner's head lamp?

The first lighting supported by the head was a candle, which was inserted into a device which could hook onto the miner's hat. The holder could also hook onto beams, coal faces and ladders and was widely used in the early 1800s. These holders were first used by Cornish miners and went over to America during the "Gold Rush" in the 1840s.

The second type of head lamp was an acetylene lamp, which was attached to the cap. The first patent granted to such a cap lamp was given to Rudolph C Kruschke of Duluth, Minnesota on 21 October 1902 (US Patent No 711 871). The lamp was named "The Brilliant Search Light" and was described as an "acetylene gas belt generator and cap burner lamp".

The third type of head lamp was an electric lamp – the type still used today. Developed in about 1910,
by 1935 these were more common than any other type of lamp.
The first batteries were liquid-powered, making them large and heavy; as a result they were worn around the waist.

As battery technology has improved, the battery as well as the lamp itself became supported by the head. However, the inventor of this system does not seem to have patented it.

The material world

Are all good thermal conductors also good electrical conductors?

The transport mechanisms for electrical and thermal conductivity are different, and they are not connected. For example, beryllia (beryllium oxide), diamond, and aluminum nitride all have high thermal conductivities and are very poor electrical conductors. As for materials that are the other way around, that's trickier. Scientists haven't yet been able to create a material which is a good electrical conductor and a bad thermal conductor. One example where they have been attempting to do this is with Half-Heusler alloys. These materials are being developed for high-temperature power generation applications. Currently they have a very high electrical conductivity and a high thermopower (temperature-induced voltage). Unfortunately, they also have a relatively high thermal conductivity. The goal is that if they can decrease the thermal conductivity of the material, they can increase the power factor (power output) since the less heat the material conducts (and dissipates) the more will be available to produce power.

If you mix water and cornflour (in a ratio of about 1:3) you get a viscous liquid that can be stirred slowly but appears to solidify if you try to stir it fast. What is happening?

A mixture of water and cornflour in the correct proportion gives what's called a dilatant liquid. It means that when a force is applied to it, the viscosity increases – ie, it gets thicker. Other materials, such as a mixture of sand and water, can also exhibit this property. Uncooked cornflour consists of small globules of starch – long chains of molecules all coiled up to form a ball. When mixed with water, the cornflour forms a suspension of starch particles in the water. Imagine the starch particles as little spheres. If you have the right proportion, then the starch particles are all in close contact with one another, and the water fills the gaps in between. This water acts as a lubricant so that the starch particles can flow past one another if pushed slowly. That allows the mixture to flow. However, if the mixture is subject to a faster perturbation, such as stirring, then the water is squeezed out of the gaps between the particles. The starch particles now lack their lubrication, and so they become far harder to push past one another – the mixture becomes more viscous.

When water is blown out of a snow-maker it freezes to make snow, but what stops it freezing in the pipe?

When snow is formed naturally it happens because water vapour cools and condenses on to particles in the atmosphere. These particles are part of the "atmospheric aerosol" which is composed of particles from industry, sea salt, dust and dirt. Without these particles, lower temperatures would be needed to allow the formation of ice particles in clouds.

Although the water used in snow makers will be cold and will contain particles to act as condensation nuclei, more such particles are often added to increase snow production.

Why does a helium balloon pop at a certain height?

The helium gas exerts a certain pressure on the balloon from the inside. The pressure, or push of the gas molecules on the inside will be equal to the pressure on the outside of the balloon, otherwise the balloon would squish or expand. As the balloon gets higher in the sky the air pressure surrounding it decreases, resulting in a higher pressure on the inside. This means the gas molecules on the inside are pushing more on the balloon. The balloon is not infinitely elastic, so once pushed beyond its limit, it pops.

What is tensile strength, and why is it important to know the tensile strength of materials?

Tensile strength is the force needed to stretch a material until it breaks. Take bridge-building, for example: suspension bridges are built by hanging the bridge from a steel "rope" under tension. When designing the bridge it is important to know under what force the steel breaks at, to be sure the bridge will hold up.

Which metal has the greatest density?

The densest metals are those at the end of the periodic table, as their atomic nuclei have lots of protons and neutrons, but they don't take up that much more space than the nuclei of lighter atoms of elements. So there's more mass in about the same space.

At room temperature and pressure Unniloctium (element 108) has an estimated density of 41g per cubic centimetre – but nobody has ever made that much. Of naturally occurring metals, osmium is the densest: 22.57g/cc at a temperature of 298° Kelvin. In comparison, mercury is just 13.53 g/cc.

What is white spirit made of?

It is a mixture of spirits produced by heating petroleum – itself a mixture of hundreds of organic compounds with boiling points varying between 115°C and 180°C. In this temperature range, various compounds vaporise, and can be collected and used. Boiling a substance at different temperatures to give different products is called fractionation.

Salt is made of crystals, as are diamonds. Why are diamonds much harder?

Diamond is a macro-molecular structure of carbon atoms, where each carbon is bonded to four others by sharing electrons with them in a covalent bond. Salt consists of sodium and chloride ions, but these are bonded ionically, meaning one or more electrons from one atom (in this case sodium) are "given" to the other atom in the molecule. Because ionic bonds don't involve sharing electrons between atoms, they aren't as strong as covalent bonds. This is why diamonds are stronger than salt.

Adding Dettol to water makes it cloudy. Why? What is it that makes two liquids go cloudy?

Dettol and water goes cloudy because Dettol contains substances that are not soluble in water. Some solids or liquids will dissolve or mix more easily in one type of liquid than another. For example, oil and water do not mix; and salt will dissolve in water, but not in oil. Solubility depends on the chemical composition and structure of the substances involved.

The major constituents of Dettol are pine oil, which has disinfectant properties, and alcohol. Pine oil dissolves in alcohol but not in water.

Mixing the Dettol into water makes it more dilute until there is not enough alcohol to keep the pine oil dissolved. It then "drops out" of the water and becomes a fine suspension – making it cloudy.

How much lead is there in lead crystal? And how is it that we can see through it?

The amount of lead depends on the type of crystal: English lead crystal contains more than 30 per cent. But the lead is in the form of lead oxide, not the pure metal, just as ordinary glass is made from silica – an oxide of silicon, an opaque metal in its pure form. The lead oxide forms a random structure in the glass – and, like the silica, it lets light through.

What is the strongest plant fibre?

A fibre called ramie is the strongest. Its fibres are eight times as strong as those of cotton.

What is actually inside a bacterium?

Bacteria are simple cells; they do not have a distinct nucleus and they do not have many of the organelles (such as mitochondria, chloroplasts, and endoplasmic reticulum) that a higher organism's cells have.

The size and shape of bacteria varies according to their type, but they all have a cell wall, a cell membrane and a rather untidy mass of DNA in the middle of their cytoplasm. The cytoplasm itself is granular and not organised into compartments – enzymes and the protein-making ribosomes exist freely.

Some bacteria have long hair-like structures on their outer surface called flagellae, which are important in movement: they can be rotated to act like a propeller, moving the bacterium about in the liquid in which it lives.

Do bacteria have sex?

Bacteria normally reproduce asexually, by simply splitting into two identical cells. However, some bacteria do actually mate. As well as long "hairs"

called flagellae, bacteria have smaller hair-like structures on their surface, called pili. One bacteria can join pili with another bacteria, forming a continuous tube between the two cells.

Genetic information called plasmids – little loops of DNA – can then pass from one bacterium to another. Bacterial mating and passing of plasmids are important for two main reasons.

First, that is how bacteria pass on the genes for certain types of antibiotic resistance: passing these genes between generations, as well as down through the generation, means that more bacteria become antibiotic-resistant more quickly (which suits the bacteria, though not humans).

The other reason is that this process is useful to molecular biologists for their research.

Silicon is similar to carbon. Why are there no life forms based on silicon?

Silicon is unsuitable as a basis for life because, although it is a valency IV element like carbon, the Si-Si covalent bond is not strong enough for it to form long stable chains, unlike the C-C bond. Silicon cannot therefore form molecules of the complexity needed to make up cells.

Do all woods float?

Any wood (in fact, any object) with a density greater than the density of water will sink. Tallow wood, Queensland Red Ironwood and certain types of ebony are all examples of woods that will sink.

What are the most expensive elements?

That depends to some extent on what state they are sold in – for example, as foil, wire, powder, rod, etc. Generally speaking, however, the most expensive elements are osmium, platinum, iridium, gold and europium.

How are diamonds made?

A synthetic diamond is made from graphite under high temperatures and pressures. It differs from a natural diamond in size, shape and the number of impurities. It is made specifically for industry.

Natural diamonds, by contrast, are made over millions of years from carbon sources in the Earth. But they, too, were made using high temperatures and pressures.

What are parachutes made of, and how long do they last?

Early parachutes used to be made of silk, but silk hasn't been used in the manufacture of parachutes for some 50 years now. Instead, manufacturers generally use rip-stop nylon, which is made of lots of tiny squares which prevent a rip from propagating along its length.

A parachute will typically last for around 10 or 12 years, or 100 jumps (whichever comes first), before it needs to be replaced. Of course, it can be damaged before that – usually as a result of damage sustained on landing. A standard person-carrying parachute requires about 100 square metres of material.

Is it possible to insulate things from magnetism? If so, how?

Any object will become magnetised in the presence of a magnet. Often this is a temporary state, and as the magnet is moved away the object will be demagnetised. A few materials can be permanently magnetised.

A screen (as it is called) from magnetism must be highly magnetisable (but only temporarily). A good substance for this is "mu" metal alloy, which is an alloy in which two-thirds is iron and one-third nickel.

The object to be shielded is put inside a cylinder of the shield. When an external magnetic field is applied the shield, the shield becomes magnetised, but the magnetic forces are limited to the surround of the cylinder; it shields the object inside from being magnetised. You can buy mu alloy metal, but you must get it already in the desired shape - any bending or hitting of the mu metal stops it working.

Do tachyons go faster than the speed of light?

A tachyon is a theoretical particle that is supposed to travel faster than the speed of light. They are also supposed to generate a special type of radiation and physicists have been looking for this radiation for the last 20 years. Seeing as nobody has ever found this radiation or a tachyon, it rather suggests the tachyons were a result of a glitch in our mathematical theories, rather than the theory of relativity itself.

Boiling water kills germs and bacteria, but what does freezing water do to them?

It depends on the bacteria. If you put samples of E. coli or salmonella into ice they will stop growing, but they will survive maybe a month or more. Other species are more delicate. For example, campylobacter, which causes food poisoning, grows at 37°C to 42°C. The bacteria generally die at temperatures below room temperature, although they can be stored alive at -80°C if they are frozen very fast under the right conditions.

There is a group of microbes called psychrophiles which thrive in freezing environments, for example in Antarctic sea ice (ocean water that is frozen for much of the year). Apart from these specially adapted organisms, however, freezing conditions generally stop the growth of bacteria, even though they cannot be guaranteed to kill them.

First principles

Has life been created in the laboratory? That is, has anyone made a primordial soup in a lab, sent a spark through it and ended up with life?

It has proven possible to produce some of the very basic units of life from basic elements. But to get those into the correct form and to produce the complex chemicals for life would be extremely difficult. It is very hard to produce the long stretches of DNA necessary even to code for the most basic of creatures. DNA has evolved to be copied; producing it from scratch is more difficult. Even if you do make the DNA, you then have to make all the proteins which form the DNA into chromosomes, and then all of the enzymes, nucleic acids, fats and carbohydrates which make up the cell. Then those chemicals have to be built into the structures that form the cell. Although it may be theoretically possible, the technology to be able to do it in the lab still evades us. There have been

billions of years of evolution to make the creation of organisms possible. To try to replicate that in the lab is extremely inefficient. It's much easier to do it naturally.

Is the calculation of *pi* empirical (by measurement) or theoretical?

Pi is a constant – but it is an "irrational" number, meaning it cannot be exactly expressed as the ratio of two numbers. So it can never be completely enumerated, only approximated: it is the sum of an infinite series. But the fact that *pi* is constant has been known for so long that it is quite untraceable. In very ancient times, 3 was used as the approximate value of *pi* – almost certainly derived from measurement.

It seems that Archimedes, in the third century BC, was the first person to make a scientific effort to compute it. By calculating the circumference of a 96-sided polygon, he showed the value was between $223/71$ and $22/7$ – that is, to one per cent accuracy.

The precision of *pi* has increased steadily throughout history but it was not until the introduction of computers this century that it could be calculated to many decimal places. Nowadays computer algorithms can express it to millions of digits.

What are fractals?

In mathematics, fractals are a class of complex geometric shapes. They are distinct from the simple figures of classical – or Euclidean – geometry (the square, circle, sphere, and so forth), being capable of describing the many irregularly-shaped objects (such as snowflakes) or spatially non-uniform phenomena in nature that cannot be accommodated by the components of Euclidean geometry. The term, from the Latin word fractus ("fragmented," or "broken"), was coined by the Polish-born mathematician Benoit B. Mandelbrot. Since its introduction in 1975, the concept has given rise to a system of geometry that has had a significant impact on mathematics, physical chemistry, physiology, and fluid mechanics.

What is the equation for the Mandelbrot plot?

The Mandelbrot fractal set is given by the iterative equation $Z_{n+1} = Z_n^2 + c$ where Z and c are allowed to assume complex values such as $2 + i$ (where i is the [imaginary] square root of -1.)

What does E=mc² actually mean?

That energy is the same kind of "thing" as mass, except it's expressed in a different way. (This really is a very profound fact about the Universe.) It also means that energy can be turned into mass and mass can be turned into energy.

E stands for energy, the *m* stands for mass, and *c* is the speed of light - already a large number which gets even bigger (90,000,000,000,000,000 J/kg or so) when you square it. That is the exchange rate between mass and energy: the power released in an atomic explosion comes from that conversion. The Hiroshima bomb, with just 10kg of plutonium, only actually converted about 1g into pure energy – but it was enough to wipe out a city.

How many radians are there in 360 degrees?

Radians are another way of measuring angles, rather like kilometres and miles being two different scales for measuring the same distances. Radians are widely used in engineering, and are defined so that there are 2 x *pi* radians in a complete circle. Because it is not a round number (it has an infinite decimal expansion), radians are not often used where real measurements are made; they are more commonly applied to theoretical applications. Another method of measuring angles is gradians: there are 400 of these in a full circle, and they are used by navigators – if you travel 100km in a straight line on the earth's surface, you have gone 1 gradian around the centre of the planet.

How are mathematical shapes named?

Shapes are named from the standard Greek roots for numbers, according to the number of sides: for example, pentagon (five), hexagon (six), heptagon/ septagon (seven), octagon (eight), enneagon/nonagon (nine), decagon (10), hendecagon/ undecagon (11), dodecagon (12).

Three- and four-sided figures are so familiar that we usually talk of the triangle and quadrilateral rather than the formal "trigon" and "tetragon". But most names for large numbers of sides are not used: a 27-sided shape is just called "a 27-sided polygon". Exceptions to this include the 15-sided pendecagon/ quindecagon and the 1,000-sided chiliagon.

What are the names for quarks?

Of the six forms of quark, the first two discovered (in the late 1960s) were classified as "up" and "down". The third was found in a very odd particle (called a K meson) so it was called "strange". The fourth was named "charm" because someone thought it was a smart name. This was not as bad as the names originally given to the last two: "truth" and "beauty". Their names were changed to "bottom" and "top". The top

quark was not confirmed found until 1994.

Are there such things as leap seconds?

Yes. Because of how we measure time, we sometimes need to add leap seconds to match up our clocks with the actual position of the Earth around the Sun. The rotation of the Earth about its axis isn't exactly even, which makes the days vary in length. These slight changes didn't matter until 1967, when atomic clocks were invented and the second was defined as a certain number of oscillations of a caesium atom. This definition is what gives us International Atomic Time (TAI). But the TAI isn't based on the earth's rotation, so a calendar based on TAI gradually becomes out of step with one based on GMT. We could use TAI as our official time (and in fact we do, with slight alterations of leap seconds) but then the time would get out of step with day and night and the seasons. So for convenience we use GMT and adjust TAI accordingly. In 1972 a new Coordinated Universal Time scale (UTC) was adopted for international use. It combines all the regularity of atomic time with most of the convenience of GMT. The seconds of UTC are of the same length as those of TAI, and then UTC is kept within one second of GMT by the insertion of extra leap seconds.

The last leap second was added to the world's clocks on the stroke of midnight on 31 December 2006.

What is Russian multiplication?

Russian or peasant multiplication is multiplication by repeated doubling. For example, to multiply 17 by 13 you double the 17 and halve the 13, and add the doubles that correspond to an odd number in the other column. Like this: 17 x 13 – doubled and halved: 34 x 6 (add 17); doubled and halved: 68 x 3 (add 68); doubled and halved: 136 x 1.
So the answer is 136 + 68 +17 = 221. This may seem a cumbersome way of doing things, but it is a handy way of writing long multiplication in binary.

How does the sulphur dioxide emission of smokeless fuels compare with that of coal?

Generally speaking, smokeless fuels are made with less sulphur than ordinary coal.
  This means that they will produce less sulphur dioxide when they are burnt, and so should contribute less to acid rain and similar effects.

How do halogen lamps work?

A conventional light bulb, filled with an inert gas such as argon, is limited to a certain temperature: the tungsten filament gradually evaporates and condenses on the cooler glass envelope, and a very bright bulb would wear out too quickly. A halogen bulb enables the filament to run at a higher temperature, hence is brighter. Halogens – fluorine, chlorine, bromine, iodine and astatine – are highly reactive. A tungsten halide (usually tungsten iodide) is the key: it is stable at low temperature, but unstable when very hot. When the tungsten evaporates from the hot filament it forms a vapour which cools as it nears the outer glass, and reacts with the iodine to form tungsten iodide. This itself is stable until it comes into contact with the very hot filament, where it dissociates into its elements. Tungsten is redeposited on the filament, releasing iodine vapour to repeat the cycle.

Why doesn't a rocket topple over on take-off when the supports are withdrawn?

The supports are only withdrawn when the jets at the bottom of the rocket are supporting its weight. It is a question of split-second timing. If you watch a launch countdown carefully, you will see that the rockets are ignited before zero and while the rocket is still held in place. Once the jets have fired up enough to support the rocket – which happens almost instantaneously – the supports are removed.

How is a hologram made?

A hologram is the result of wave interference between two laser beams, which contain light of a single frequency. One laser beam is shone directly on to a plate covered by a light-sensitive emulsion, like a photographic plate, while another is shone on to an object and then on to the plate.

One beam thus has further to travel than the other. Where they meet, the difference in distance means their wavefronts are out of phase with each other. They "interfere" to create patterns like those formed when two stones are dropped into a pond. These interference patterns are recorded by the plate, and recreated when a light is shone on to the plate afterwards. We perceive those recreated patterns as a picture of the object that created the interference.

How was the Turin shroud shown to date from the Middle Ages, not from the time of Jesus?

By carbon dating. Carbon-14 is a radioactive isotope of carbon, produced when cosmic rays hit nitrogen-14 nuclei in the atmosphere. It has a half-life of 5,700 years. The proportion in the atmosphere stays constant. However, animals and plants, which while they are alive contain the same ratio of carbon-14 atoms to stable carbon-12 atoms as the atmosphere, stop exchanging atoms with their surroundings when they die. So the proportion of carbon-14 falls as the atoms decay.

When it has halved, for example, the specimen is 5,700 years old. This dating method can be used for any organic material, such as bone, wood or cloth.

One problem is knowing the concentration of carbon-14 in ancient times; fortunately, wood can also be dated by tree-ring measurements. Modern techniques can measure the ratio of carbon-14 to carbon-12 using very small samples - small enough for the Pope to give his consent for one to be taken from the shroud. It was found in 1988 to be no more than 750 years old.

How do we dispose safely of CFCs?

All local authorities should now offer a degassing service for fridges and other CFC-containing devices. The material recovered can easily be reused depending on how contaminated it is. For example, fridge companies can just filter and remove moisture from the gas before using it again. But if it is taken by local councils, it might need to be distilled to separate out the different CFCs so that it can be used in different applications. The material extracted by local councils is controlled by several central organisations, and fines are imposed on those who let the gases out uncontrolled.

How fast is Mach 8, and can military aircraft travel that quickly?

Mach 8 (measured at 0°C) is eight times the speed of sound, about 9,500km/h (6,000mph). The fastest unclassified military aircraft is the SR-71 Blackbird reconnaissance plane, with a sustained cruise speed of a little more than Mach 3. As Mach 1 is the speed of sound, Mach 1 to 5 is "supersonic flight"; Mach 6 and over is "hypersonic flight". This has been achieved only by the X-15 research aircraft and the Space Shuttle re-entering the atmosphere (at Mach 25!). There are persistent rumours of a classified military project, "Aurora", which appears to involve a hypersonic reconnaissance vehicle, but these remain unconfirmed.

How do doctors look inside brains without surgery?

The oldest technique is X-ray imaging. X-rays are good for examining skull fractures, but reveal little about the fine structure of soft brain tissues. An improvement came with computerised tomography (CT), which uses a series of small X-ray beams at different angles to one another to give a more detailed picture. CT gives pictures of a slice of brain (tomos is the Greek word for "cut") which help diagnose many brain diseases.

In positron emission tomography (PET), the patient is injected with weakly radioactive compounds. A scanner picks up the radioactivity emitted, indicating where the blood is being used - ie, where the brain is working hardest. Such scans are useful not just for diagnosing brain problems, but also to understand how a healthy brain works.

More recently, magnetic resonance imaging (MRI) has become popular. It can detect the presence of a particular substance in the brain by scanning for its unique chemical "signature". The images produced are amazingly detailed, but it's an expensive means of getting them.

How do the widgets in beer cans work?

Widgets - devices in the bottom of beer cans to give a frothy head - consist of a plastic container of nitrogen with a closed valve. The widget is placed in the can; then beer is added along with a small amount of nitrogen to fill the small gap between the top of the beer and the can. The beer is pasteurised, and the heat expands the widget and increases pressure in the can. When it's opened, the pressure bursts the valve in the widget and lets out the nitrogen. This gives smaller bubbles that last longer and look whiter.

Does a bullet still accelerate once it has left the barrel of a gun?

No. It begins to decelerate as soon as it leaves the barrel, or even before if the barrel is long, because there is no new impulse applied. A bullet fired horizontally from a gun held one metre off the ground will hit the ground at the same time as a pebble dropped from someone's hand at the same time and height - about half a second later.

SERIES CONTINUES TOMORROW: Free with 'The Independent', an exclusive 12-part series of 'Science made simple' mini-books, demystifying the key concepts of science, begins on Monday with 'The Earth'